UNDERSTANDING DIGITAL TECHNOLOGY

G000139954

by

F. A. WILSON
C.G.I.A., C.Eng., F.I.E.E., F.I.Mgt.

BERNARD BABANI (publishing) LTD
THE GRAMPIANS
SHEPHERDS BUSH ROAD
LONDON W6 7NF
ENGLAND

Other Titles of Interest

Preface

Knowledge is of two kinds. We know a subject ourselves,
or we know where we can find information upon it.
Samuel Johnson (1709–1784)

Life seems to becoming all *digital* nowadays, yet a few decades
ago the term was unheard of. What is it all about and how will
it affect us? This book is effectively an educational chat about
digital technology and its rôle in modern society.
Unquestionably the full explanation is very involved and ongoing – it would fill many books the size of this one.

Technology is steadily pushing us away from the way of life
we used to know towards one in which our actions are dictated
by that infinitesimally small speck of what we call electricity,
the electron. How millions of them get together to do some of
the amazing things we now take for granted is our subject.
Digital technology has arrived in all its glory and woe betide
any of us, the electronics people of this world, who fail to
understand at least what makes it tick and how it provides a
new service to mankind. There are clearly many budding electronics engineers who know a little about the subject and would
like to know more, but not to any great mathematical depth.
This book is mainly for them but it also has appeal to those who
already understand the fundamentals but wish to expand their
knowledge.

Several Appendices have been added to explain some of the
concepts more fully or perhaps to remind us of the things we
once knew about but by now have forgotten. A glossary of
many of the terms associated with digital technology is also
there.

F. A. Wilson

Please Note

Although every care has been taken with the production of this book to ensure that any projects, designs, modifications and/or programs, etc., contained herewith, operate in a correct and safe manner and also that any components specified are normally available in Great Britain, the Publishers do not accept responsibility in any way for the failure, including fault in design, of any project, design, modification or program to work correctly or to cause damage to any other equipment that it may be connected to or used in conjunction with, or in respect of any other damage or injury that may be so caused, nor do the Publishers accept responsibility in any way for the failure to obtain specified components.

Notice is also given that if equipment that is still under warranty is modified in any way or used or connected with home-built equipment then that warranty may be void.

© 1995 BERNARD BABANI (publishing) LTD

First Published – September 1995

British Library Cataloguing in Publication Data

Wilson, F. A.

Understanding Digital Technology

I. Title

621.3815

ISBN 0 85934 376 6

Printed and bound in Great Britain by Cox & Wyman Ltd, Reading

Contents

Chapter 1

THE CASE FOR DIGITAL

There is no doubt that our own ability in handling numbers is limited. There are those among us who can successfully complete most complex computations mentally but their number is few. Nowadays most of us immediately seek the help of some sort of electronic device to do the calculations for us. Such help however was not always available.

As our ancestors became capable of measuring time, distance, temperature and many other phenomena, came the need for calculation. The *abacus* which had already been in use in the East since time immemorial and was still around, had its uses. It is a device using beads sliding on wires which is capable of addition, subtraction, multiplication and division and in fact is still in use today by some small children. We ourselves needed something better as our horizons began to expand and in 1621 came the slide-rule which enables quick calculations to be made mathematically through the use of logarithms but with only fair accuracy. Then in 1642 Blaise Pascal (the French scientist and mathematician) produced the first calculating machine, a move in the right direction but it could only add and subtract. Following this along came Gottfried Leibniz (a German scientist) with his machine capable also of multiplication and division. These machines were crude and slow but they certainly pointed the way to greater possibilities.

So much went on until in 1889 Dr Herman Hollerith designed his "electric tabulator", the first successful data processing machine. Subsequently development of the computer really got under way until by 1946 the ENIAC (Electronic Numerical Integrator And Computer), the first completely electronic machine arrived. It relied entirely on thermionic valves, hence maintenance was a nightmare. However in the 1960's semiconductors came along and although the maintenance problem was not fully solved, it was certainly eased.

Fully electronic operation gave us a speed in calculations never known before. This is not surprising when we recall that an electrical impulse in the shape of a radio wave can travel

1

seven times round the earth in only one second. Within a computer therefore operations take an almost infinitesimally short time and in fact electrical impulses follow one another at a rate of millions every *second*.

Most computers are *digital*, a description into which we will enquire later. Digital technology has not stopped there, it is now the basis of many of our transmission systems e.g. for both world-wide and even local telephony. In fact digital technology has not only come to stay, it is to a great extent destined to take over, except for our good selves of course for peculiarly enough we are unable to join in and so remain basically *analogue*.

1.1 Information

Digital technology is all about providing and storing information or simply moving it around. *Information* is that intangible something which leads to enlightenment through communication, the term is linked closely with *knowledge*. More precisely, information is defined as 'the reduction of uncertainty'. If there is no uncertainty then there is no requirement for information. As an example, if the date is already known, there is no uncertainty and hence no information is gained by studying a calendar. Scientists began to be interested in the quantitative (measurement of quantity) theory of information flow in the 1920's and by 1948 the science of *cybernetics* had been born. This is a study of the general philosophy of control and communication. At the same time C. E. Shannon (an American mathematician) really set the ball rolling in the study of information flow in communication systems. In essence he attempted to analyse and quantify information, a most difficult endeavour. From his work it became possible to calculate the rate of information flow for any electrical waveform. The formulae he developed indicated clearly that it is not simply the bandwidth of a channel which determines just how much information can be transmitted over it in a given time but also the *signal-to-noise ratio*. (A channel is simply the path over which information is passed. It could be a complicated satellite link or simply the air-path between a talker and a listener in a room.) Noise in a communication system is therefore an embarrassment to information flow and in telecommunications it is considered as being any spurious electrical disturbance occurring

2

within the channel. Noise gets into a communication channel from many sources and we will see how it is detrimental to digital transmission in Section 5.4.4.

1.2 Analogue and Digital

Firstly we must get to grips with the principles of digital transmission and how it differs from analogue. The latter is from the Greek meaning *proportional to*, hence implies similarity or something parallel, a good example being the electrical output of a microphone. Viewed on a cathode-ray oscilloscope, the waveform is simply a graph of the microphone output voltage on the basis of time, this itself follows the vibrations of the talker's vocal cords. The whole system is analogue for the ultimate electrical waveform is similar or parallel to that generated originally. Essentially an analogue system therefore carries a continuous waveform.

A digital system on the other hand works entirely on pulses. The word *digital* is derived from Latin, *digitus*, a finger. The pulses carry information just as an analogue signal does and a unit of information mainly in use in pulse systems is known as a 'bit'. It is defined as the selection between two equally probable events i.e. at a certain specified time there can be either a pulse or no pulse and the receiver has no prior knowledge as to which it will be. This is our *binary* system and it is the one in almost universal use for digital working.

The question immediately arises as to why digital when we ourselves are mainly analogue? It would appear that whenever we humans are involved, a digital system must be capable of accepting analogue information at its input and of delivering in analogue at the output. The so-called digital computer provides an example. It cannot be fully digital for it has to communicate with the outside world via its keyboard and screen. This must be so and it involves us in an added complication but overall digital systems have many advantages. An analogue signal transmitted over a line can suffer many distortions and from the addition of noise picked up on the way. The signal is reduced in amplitude as it travels owing to line attenuation. It may be considered that there is no problem here for we have amplifiers which can easily restore a signal to its original amplitude but note now that it is a distorted signal which is amplified together with the noise picked up on the way. Accordingly the longer the circuit, the more the noise which is added hence the signal-to-noise ratio is reduced. We can look at this more technically by using a general formula from Shannon (Sect.1.1) relating channel capacity with bandwidth when noise is present:

$$C = W \log_2 (1 + s/n) \text{ bits per second}$$

where C is the channel capacity, W is the channel bandwidth (Hz) and s/n is the channel signal-to-noise ratio. Tables of logarithms to the base 2 do not abound in plenty so Appendix 1 is added relating $\log_2 (1 + s/n)$ with signal-to-noise ratios, quoted also in decibels.

Evidently what is important is the degree by which the signal level exceeds that of the noise. Just two examples may illustrate the usefulness of the formula although we must be mindful of the difficulties we may encounter in using mathematics to describe cases of information flow.

Taking a rather extreme case, with a signal-to-noise ratio of 0.5 (amplitude of noise twice that of the signal), the channel capacity (in bits per second) is 0.585 of the channel bandwidth. This indicates that a high level of noise on a channel reduces its effective capacity for the transmission of information considerably. On the other hand a signal-to-noise ratio of 10 (signal level 10 times that of the noise) allows a channel capacity of over 3 times the channel bandwidth. The gain in information flow when channel noise is reduced is clearly shown.

Digital pulses of course suffer the same problems of distortion over a line (but not for example *within* a computer) i.e. where a transmitter and receiver are separated at a distance. However instead of using amplifiers as for analogue the digital systems employ *regenerators*. Provided that the pulses are recognizable as such, regenerators detect them and generate completely new ones, hence noise and distortions are not passed on. Theoretically therefore the pulses at the receiving end of a circuit, irrespective of its length, are 'as new'.

1.3 The Digital Signal
We concentrate on the binary system because as mentioned

above, it is used almost to the exclusion of the various other methods of information transfer. The system is not new for although we ourselves are essentially analogue, by nodding the head for "yes" and shaking it for "no", we are unwittingly going binary digital. Clearly the yes/no principle has much to recommend it when it is appropriate for there is no doubt as to the message. Take the Spanish Armada as an early example. In 1588 bonfires lit to indicate its impending arrival were in fact working digital, simply a yes/no information system. Later on we had the dash and dot of the Morse Code and later still the mark and space of the telegraph code. In this system marks were written on a moving paper tape. Accordingly instead of trying to work with 10 different states as in our decimal system, there is much less likelihood of error if only the two which are recognized with the greatest certainty are used.

Nowadays computers and transmission systems are based on the binary digit or *bit* and generally the two binary states are denoted by the decimal numbers 0 and 1. Note how closely this "bit" is linked with Shannon's in the previous Section. The binary 0 is indicated by no (or very little) voltage, the 1 by some voltage of sufficient value to be easily distinguishable from the 0. For transmission systems where as shown above, noise may be a problem, the near certainty of being able to distinguish between a 0 and a 1 makes binary ideal for digital working.

So often do we see the term *logic* used. It is technically an arrangement of elements to perform a specified task. However the word is often used rather loosely, it is usually applied to the circuitry e.g. a *logic gate* as will be seen later but it may also be applied to the signals which operate such gates e.g. *logic 0* and *logic 1*. In the latter case however we can often be forgiven for omitting the term *logic* and simply using 0 and 1.

1.4 The Pulse

Next we come to the pulse itself, the very heart of digital technology. It is the digit in electrical form which we must now examine in all its aspects. Generally a pulse is a tiny affair and is used in almost unbelievable numbers. Let us first examine what is perhaps a rather extreme case but certainly a practical one. This is a 2 Gb/s fibre-optic system (2 thousand million bits per *second* – see Appendix 2 for units and prefixes). With the more recent fibre-optic systems information can be passed over special glass fibres of diameter similar to that of a human hair. Compared with all other systems the bandwidths obtainable are extensive and unheard of until recently. Accordingly for this particular system the duration of a single pulse is a mere 500 picoseconds (500×10^{-12} s). One might be forgiven for wondering whether many electrons would be around during such a short time but it can be shown for example, that for a 10 mA pulse of this duration there would be over 30 million of them. Looking at it from the telephony point of view, it is now easy to appreciate that there may be as many as 20 000 telephone calls travelling over a single fibre. However not all telephony is conducted over fibre-optic systems. In contrast to talking in terms of thousands of voice circuits over a single system, in the early part of this century overhead copper wires weighing as much as 600 lbs (about 270 kg) per mile were required to transmit one single voice circuit over a moderately long trunk. Our progress in electronics is truly phenomenal.

An "ideal" pulse is sketched in Figure 1.1. This is a *rectangular* pulse which rises to its maximum, continues at that level

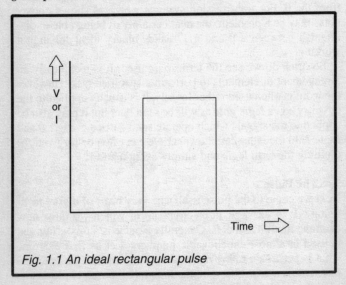

Fig. 1.1 An ideal rectangular pulse

for a short time and then decreases to zero. Both rise and fall theoretically occur instantaneously. However it is clear that such an ideal pulse cannot exist for the transitions between maximum and minimum must take time. Some pulse generators are capable of producing pulses approaching the ideal shown in the Figure but here we are mainly concerned with what can happen to a pulse especially when it is roving far from home.

The French mathematician, Jean Baptiste Joseph Fourier in the early 1800's produced what we now call *Fourier Analysis*. He developed the mathematics to show how complex waveforms (e.g. a rectangular wave) can be analysed. What may be surprising is that his formulae showed that a square-cornered pulse can be expressed as the sum of a number of sine waves. Now it may be difficult at first to relate a square or rectangular wave to the more graceful sine wave but Figure 1.2 may help. Fourier has shown that to transmit the pulse of Figure 1.1 over a circuit while maintaining its shape, requires that the circuit should have infinite bandwidth, a condition which is unobtainable.

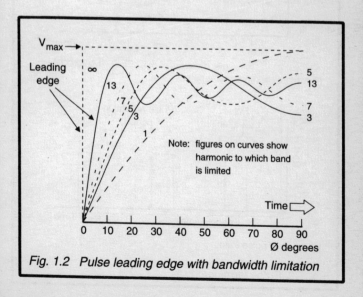

Fig. 1.2 Pulse leading edge with bandwidth limitation

In Figure 1.2 we consider the leading edge of a rectangular pulse only, similar conditions apply to the trailing edge. The theoretical condition of infinite bandwidth is shown and it is evident that as the bandwidth restriction increases, a rectangular pulse degenerates towards a sine wave – a clear indication that the pulse sides will slope. A good circuit which passes up to the 13th harmonic shows a fairly steep rise but of course to include the 13th harmonic is rather expensive on bandwidth hence it must be accepted that generally a pulse will have a rise time (defined later) typically as sketched in Figure 1.3(i). Equally there will be a decay time as also shown. Reactances present in the circuit also delay the build-up and decay e.g. if the pulse is to be transmitted over a line having capacitance,

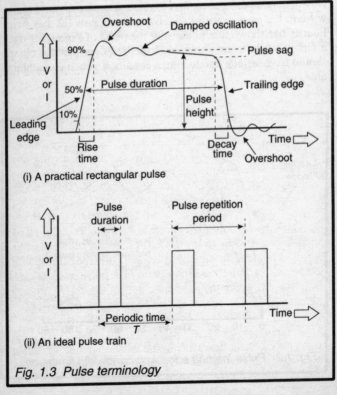

(i) A practical rectangular pulse

(ii) An ideal pulse train

Fig. 1.3 Pulse terminology

this has to be charged at the expense of the pulse itself, so increasing the rise time. Also when the pulse ceases, discharge of the line capacitance increases the pulse decay time.

Figure 1.3 shows most of the labels describing a practical pulse:

(1) *leading edge* is the portion of the pulse which first increases in amplitude;

(2) *trailing edge* is the portion of the pulse when it is decaying to the base level;

(3) *pulse height* is the average level maintained at the high level;

(4) *pulse duration or width* is the time between the 50% maximum amplitude points on the leading and trailing edges;

(5) *rise time* is the time during which the leading edge rises from 10% to 90% of the pulse height;

(6) *decay time* is the time during which the trailing edge falls from 90% to 10% of the pulse height;

(7) *pulse sag (or droop)* occurs when the top part of the characteristic falls slightly below the nominal pulse height value;

(8) *overshoot* can occur when the pulse rises to a value above the pulse height. It is frequently followed by a damped oscillatory condition (see also Fig.1.2). This condition can also occur at the base level.

When similar pulses occur regularly, this is known as a *pulse train* and a typical train of ideal pulses is shown in Figure 1.3(ii). The periodic time, *T*, between corresponding points is known as the pulse *repetition period* (or *pulse spacing*) so the frequency at which the pulses are transmitted is $1/T$, measured in hertz. This is known as the *pulse repetition frequency*.

1.4.1 Generation
Considering what can happen to a pulse in action as indicated above it is clear that the generated pulse should start out as near perfect as possible. Pulse generators are used in fully

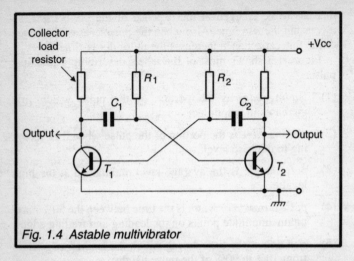

Collector
load
resistor

+Vcc

R_1 R_2

C_1 C_2

Output←

→Output

T_1 T_2

Fig. 1.4 Astable multivibrator

integrated circuit form but here we look firstly at the basic
astable multivibrator circuit (a = not) and then at circuits
embodying standard integrated circuits. An astable multivibrator is capable of providing a rectangular waveform continuously at various frequencies and with variable mark/space ratios (a
term left over from the telegraph code – see Sect.1.3).

The term *multivibrator* indicates many vibrations (or frequencies), hence it is a device with an output which is rich in
harmonics. As Figure 1.2 indicates, the more the harmonics, the
nearer the output approaches a square wave. The basic circuit
consists of two active devices, the output of each being coupled
to the input of the other. The two devices work in unison, each
controlling the other.

The essential components of an astable multivibrator are
shown in Figure 1.4. Two transistors T_1 and T_2 are required,
coupled together by the capacitors C_1 and C_2 in conjunction
with the resistors R_1 and R_2. These two resistors provide base
bias to the transistors.

Consider the initial connection of the collector supply V_{cc}.
Both transistors start to conduct because base currents are flow-
ing through the resistors R_1 and R_2. The transistors cannot be
perfectly matched hence one (say T_1) will conduct more than its

partner. With the rise in collector current of T_1, the voltage drop across its collector load increases, accordingly its collector potential falls. This applies a negative-going voltage pulse to the base of T_2 which therefore reduces its collector current, hence creating a rise in collector voltage so passing back a positive-going pulse to the base of T_1 further aiding its rise in collector current and fall in collector voltage. This reinforces the fall in potential on T_2 base. The process continues, rapidly driving T_1 into saturation and T_2 to cut-off. This condition cannot hold because with the time constants of C_1R_1 and C_2R_2 present there cannot be a permanent negative voltage held on the base of either transistor hence both circuits are unstable (i.e. the circuits cannot lock). Continuation of the circuit analysis in this way may become tedious but the final result is that the multivibrator oscillates between the two stages continuously. It is therefore classed as *free running*. At the two output terminals (Fig.1.4) therefore antiphase rectangular waveforms are available.

If, for example, both the capacitances are made equal to C and both the resistances to R, then the output can be shown to be a square wave having a pulse repetition frequency:

$$\text{p.r.f.} = \frac{1}{1.386\ CR} = \frac{0.722}{CR}\ \text{Hz}$$

where C is the capacitance in farads and R the resistance in ohms. The periodic time, T of the output waveform is the reciprocal of this, i.e. $1.386\ CR$. However when component values are not the same on both sides of the circuit, i.e. the time constants differ, then different mark/space ratios are generated. Also it is evident that with capacitors and resistors around, nothing can happen in no time, the result being a small amount of rounding off of the leading edges of the pulses. This cannot be eliminated completely but may be minimized by making the collector load resistors reasonably low. Circuit design is therefore a compromise.

Frequency stability may be improved by the application of a synchronizing signal to one of the transistor bases. Such a signal has no effect when the transistor is conducting (ON) but when it is OFF the signal ensures that the transistor switches back to ON at the right instant.

Complete astable multivibrators are available in fully integrated packages but it would be unwise of us to attempt to examine the circuit of any one of these. Capacitance is not easily built into an integrated circuit unless it is of very low value hence an integrated circuit becomes more than a little complicated because alternative circuit techniques have to be used. We can however examine two methods of producing pulses by astable multivibrators using standard integrated circuits surrounded by networks of capacitors and resistors.

(1) *Astable multivibrator embodying an operational amplifier.* The *operational amplifier* is a general purpose linear integrated circuit amplifier which is easily controlled by external circuits to do a whole range of jobs. It is a direct-coupled high gain amplifier and therefore includes no coupling capacitors. Overall it contains several hundred minute components. Figure 1.5(i) shows such an arrangement, now with the required capacitor and resistors connected externally. Note that the amplifier has two input terminals marked + and – . Using the + terminal as the input provides an output which is in phase with the input (non-inverting, i.e. there is no phase change through the amplifier). Positive feedback is therefore from output to input via the resistor chain R_2/R_3 to the + terminal when power is connected. The amplifier is therefore rapidly driven into saturation. However there is also feedback to the – input terminal (inverting) for which there is a 180° phase change through the amplifier. Accordingly the operational amplifier has both positive and negative feedback, the negative being controlled by the time constant CR_1. Within a short period of time therefore, as the charge builds up on C, the inverting input terminal will become more positive than the non-inverting terminal, hence the amplifier immediately switches over so that the output voltage goes negative and again quickly reaches saturation. C now charges in the opposite direction until the inverting terminal becomes more negative than the non-inverting terminal whereupon the circuit reverts to the positive saturated condition. Change-over is sufficiently rapid that the circuit is capable of generating a good square wave.

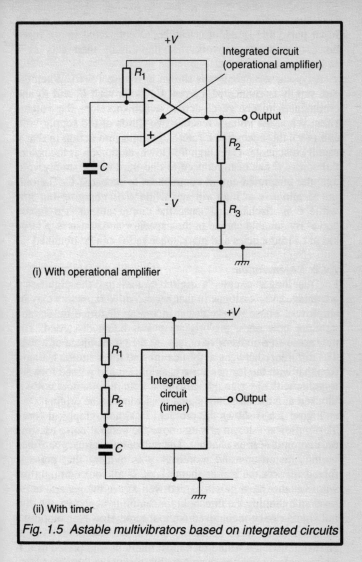

(i) With operational amplifier

(ii) With timer

Fig. 1.5 *Astable multivibrators based on integrated circuits*

(2) *Astable multivibrator with timer.* There are several integrated circuits available known as *timers*. These are capable of producing an output pulse at a given time after receipt of an

input pulse and in addition can be so connected into a resistance–capacitance network that the circuit then acts as a square-wave generator.

A typical arrangement is shown in Figure 1.5(ii). When the d.c. supply is connected, current flows through R_1 and R_2 and commences to charge C, across which therefore the voltage rises. When the voltage reaches two-thirds of the supply voltage ($+V$), the integrated circuit is brought into action in that it rapidly discharges C through R_2. However as soon as the potential across C has been reduced to one-third of the supply voltage, the integrated circuit commences to recharge C. The output terminal is at high voltage while C is charging but low while C is discharging, hence the circuit output is a square wave. By suitable choice of the capacitor and resistors, a large range of frequencies and mark/space ratios can be obtained.

1.4.2 Regeneration

For the longer circuits a digital system has the significant advantage over analogue in that *regenerative repeaters* may be employed. These simply detect incoming distorted pulses and generate new ones, the original pulses being discarded. The new noise-free undistorted pulses are then transmitted onwards. The difference between amplification and regeneration is therefore that with the former noise is amplified and passed forward together with any signal impairment, with regenerators noise is blocked and the on-going signal is as good as the original.

Figure 1.6(i) shows the problem in simple graphical form. Two pulses are shown arising above the general noise existing on a communication channel. The pulses have already suffered various distortions and moreover it is evident that noise is mixed in with the pulses themselves. It all looks straightforward because both pulses extend well above the general noise level so by setting the threshold for sampling as shown, the digital signal can be recognized without error. However suppose a spike of noise were to extend above the threshold level as shown dotted, a 0 would then most likely be interpreted as a 1. This problem might be overcome by raising the threshold level but then other difficulties may arise in that pulses might be missed altogether. Clearly then regeneration must be installed on a circuit before the pulse train has been attenuated and/or mutilated sufficiently for such errors to be possible.

Regeneration of such a signal as in Figure 1.6(i) might be accomplished by a regenerative repeater system as shown in (ii). The digital signals are first amplified and equalized. The equalizer compensates for the various types of distortion which have been introduced during the passage of the signals over the previous stage, i.e. it effectively re-shapes the pulses. Generally it is adjusted for the particular incoming line. This therefore is the first part of the cleaning-up process. From there the signals

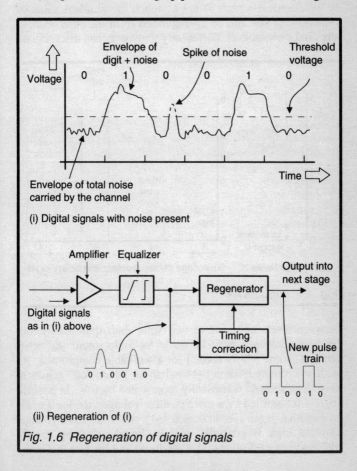

Fig. 1.6 Regeneration of digital signals

pass to the regenerator which simply detects each incoming 1 and generates a new clean pulse at the output. The time intervals between pulses may need correction so a *timing correction* circuit examines the incoming pulses and then applies a correction signal to the regenerator. A regenerator is therefore simply a controlled pulse generator.

1.4.3 Voltage Levels

What is of importance when the two logic states are represented by electrical signals is not so much the absolute value of each but that one can be distinguished from the other without any doubt whatsoever. Fortunately transistors can discriminate

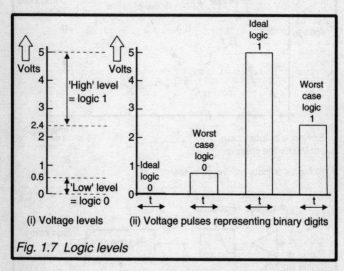

Fig. 1.7 Logic levels

between levels only one or two volts apart quite easily, but because allowance must be made for temperature and other changes, some 5 V is needed for a workable compromise. As with an ordinary electric light switch for which "off" results in zero volts so logic 0 is usually represented by 0 V. In *positive logic* 1 is signified by a more positive voltage than for 0 while in *negative logic* 1 is indicated by a more negative voltage. Positive logic is generally used in digital switching circuits although not exclusively. The variations and the fact that many

16

different devices must work to one another means that some tolerances must be put on the values and although other voltage levels may be used, most commonly found is the nominal 5 V supply. Figure 1.7(i) shows typically the range of levels transmitted in a 5 V system, hence talk about logic 1 being 5 V really means any voltage between +2.4 V and 5 V and for logic 0, 0 to 0.6 V.

Figure 1.7(ii) shows on a graph of voltage against time the acceptable pulse shapes which represent logic 0 or 1. The time *t* naturally varies from system to system and possibly within a system depending on the particular function. But to get things into perspective, we might consider it to be of the order of picoseconds up to a microsecond or so.

Chapter 2

DIGITAL ARITHMETIC

A seemingly obscure branch of mathematics came to light in the 19th century through the work of the Rev. George Boole (the English mathematician) who in 1854 published his work under the title "The Investigation of the Laws of Thought". Later John Venn and Ernst Schroder extended his ideas but to Boole goes the credit for the original development of the system of logical thinking which in fact had been around since the time of the great Greek philosopher, Aristotle. Boole's purpose was to create a better understanding of how the human mind reasons and to express this process mathematically. The ideas he developed are now known as *Boolean Algebra*, differing from our normal school algebra in that it is concerned not with add, subtract, multiply and divide, but more with classes, groups and types of objects and the relationships between them.

This all looks extremely confusing because our school algebra is deeply ingrained within us and so it is difficult for us to appreciate the alternative system, even more so to use it. As we progress however, we will find that it is not so difficult, the first hurdle simply being to clear our minds temporarily of the algebra we know so well. We confine our thoughts mainly to the use of Boolean algebra in electrical switching circuits as used in digital technology.

Logic networks are designed to control the flow of information (in the form of 0's and 1's) through an electronic system. The basic "switch" is known as a *logic gate*. Each gate is opened or closed according to information fed into its input and different types of gate can be assembled together to provide a large range of electrical switching facilities. Frequently *memory* elements are called for, these either hold digital information on a temporary basis or store it more permanently. Usually a memory element is built up from basic gates so interconnected that the information entered (0 or 1) is retained after the input signal ceases. Such elements are discussed later in Chapter 3.

2.1 Numbering Systems

Both our well-known decimal and the binary system actually work on the same basic principles. Two definitions first:

(1) an *integer* is a whole number as opposed to a *fraction* which is not a whole number and has a magnitude of between 0 and 1. In electronics we generally express fractions as one or more figures following a decimal point, e.g. 0.375 rather than as 3/8;

(2) numbers in a system are represented by a set of symbols with a *base* or *radix* (from Latin, root) which is an integer greater than 1. Our everyday example is the decimal system which employs the set of symbols 0–9 to a radix of 10. The number of symbols required is equal to the radix hence binary with its radix of 2 requires two symbols which have been borrowed from the decimal system, i.e. 0 and 1. Both these systems are known as *positional* because it is the position of each digit within the complete number which determines the actual magnitude it represents. The *most significant* digit is at the left of the number and the *least significant* at the right. Moving from left to right the values represented by each digit decrease in magnitude according to decreasing powers of the radix (explained more fully in Sect.2.1.2) hence in decimal the number 827 arises from:

$$(8 \times 10^2) + (2 \times 10^1) + (7 \times 10^0)$$

remembering that $10^0 = 1$.

The same number in binary becomes 1100111011 which is derived from:

$$(1 \times 2^9) + (1 \times 2^8) + (0 \times 2^7) + (0 \times 2^6) + (1 \times 2^5) + (1 \times 2^4) +$$

$$(1 \times 2^3) + (0 \times 2^2) + (1 \times 2^1) + (1 \times 2^0)$$

and we note that the exponent decreases by 1 at each move to the right. All this is equal to:

512 + 256 + 32 + 16 + 8 + 2 + 1, i.e. 827 in decimal.

Note that there are also other systems in use, for example, *octal* (radix 8) and *hexadecimal* (radix 16). These are used most frequently in computer systems but in no way are they as commonly found as is binary. Clearly any decimal number can be arranged to another radix. It may well be that, had prehistoric man known that computers would be invented later on, he would have chosen a numbering system based on the two arms rather than the ten fingers!

As we see above, if there are only two different digits available to represent binary numbers, the number is going to be longer than for its decimal equivalent. Take as an example the decimal number 6258. In binary this is 1100001110010, a number which fills us with misgivings owing to its sheer size with 13 digits required instead of 4. This may well convince us that we ourselves should remain decimal and leave binary to electronic systems. In fact this is how things are but it must be appreciated that electronic circuits can handle such binary numbers in nanoseconds (Appendix A2.3) or even less, so the length of a binary number, as experience shows, is far from unmanageable.

2.1.1 Bits, Bytes and Parity

As we see above, the term 'bit' is a shortened form of "binary digit". Most digital systems work with groups of bits, up to 32 or more. For convenience therefore digital signals may be assembled in basic groups of 8 bits, called *bytes*. We also find the term 'word' in use, this is usually the smallest number of bits on which the system operates. In many systems the word may consist of several bytes. The significance of the byte is that the whole range of letters, numbers, symbols and typewriter controls we use can be accommodated, in fact representation in binary of this range is by 7 bits or less (see below). A special code has been drawn up showing the binary code for each character or control, known as the American Standard Code for Information Interchange (ASCII).

We might define *combinations* as the grouping of certain numbers in every possible manner, i.e. regardless of their order. Here the certain numbers are 0 and 1 and for example, with groups of 3 we can have:

$$000 \quad 001 \quad 010 \quad 011 \quad 100 \quad 101 \quad 110 \quad 111 \ ,$$

a total of 8 which can be shown to be given by 2^3. Note that the index is the same as the number of digits in each group.

For groups of 4 bits therefore the total number of combinations is 2^4, i.e. 16.

For the 8 bits of one byte there can be up to 2^8 (= 256) different binary combinations. This is shown clearly by Appendix 4 which sets out the 256 combinations in a 16×16 table for general use as we progress.

For 7 bits there can be up to 2^7 (= 128) different combinations and this number is ample to cater for all our needs, e.g. upper and lower case letters, 10 numbers, etc. The eighth bit is employed for checking purposes. Checking is frequently required when for example, a transmission line is involved for then interference voltages encountered on the way may change a 0 to a 1 or equally a 1 to a 0. The spare checking bit is known as a *parity* bit and it is used solely as an indication that all is well. *Odd parity* adds a single logical 1 when doing so makes the total number of 1s in the word odd. *Even parity* similarly arranges for an even number of 1s. The parity bit may precede or succeed the 7 bits of the code.

As an example, the binary equivalent of the decimal number 78 is 1001110 and for 79 it is 1001111. For odd parity therefore a parity bit 1 must be added to the binary for 78 since on its own it contains an even number of 1s. Similarly, again for odd parity a parity bit 0 would be added to the binary for 79 because it already contains an odd number of 1s. Even parity is arranged in a similar way but now to ensure that the 8 bits in each case contain an even number of 1s.

At the receiving end each word is tested for the parity chosen for the particular system. A positive result in the test is a good indication of successful transmission, nevertheless with certain complex errors the technique may fail. However although there is this slight risk of failure, overall there is a greatly reduced likelihood of undetected error (see also Sect.5.1.4).

2.1.2 Binary Codes

In Section 2.1 is an introduction to binary notation and it may well be that so far we have encountered some frightening binary numbers, all of which are whole numbers. In this Section we see how a binary code (or number) is developed from the decimal equivalent. In many operations the fact that a binary sequence automatically has a decimal equivalent is of no consequence, many binary manipulations are conducted solely in binary, no reference to the decimal system being required.

As with decimals, whole binary numbers commence to the immediate left of the *binary point*. This is the binary equivalent of the decimal point and again, as with decimals, where there is no fraction, the point is omitted. Within a binary number, on moving left from the binary point, the decimal value doubles at each succeeding digit. In the opposite direction, i.e. moving right from the decimal point, the decimal value halves at each succeeding digit. Accordingly a binary number 1111.11 has a decimal equivalent of:

$$(1 \times 2^3) + (1 \times 2^2) + (1 \times 2^1) + (1 \times 2^0) . (1 \times 2^{-1}) + (1 \times 2^{-2})$$

again following the rule of a decreasing exponent on moving to the right. Note that $2^{-1} = \frac{1}{2}$ and $2^{-2} = \frac{1}{2}^2$. The result is therefore:

$$8 + 4 + 2 + 1 . 0.5 + 0.25 = 15.75$$

Where a 0 exists in the binary, no decimal value arises, e.g. 1001.01 has a decimal equivalent of:

$$(1 \times 2^3) + (1 \times 2^0) . (1 \times 2^{-2})$$

$$\text{i.e.} \quad 8 + 1 + 0.25 = 9.25$$

This is the full story including fractional numbers, happily the likelihood of requiring binary fractions is small. The relationship between decimal and binary for 0 – 20 in decimal is:

Decimal	Binary
0	0
1	1
2	10
3	11
4	100

Decimal	Binary
5	101
6	110
7	111
8	1000
9	1001
10	1010
11	1011
12	1100
13	1101
14	1110
15	1111
16	10000
17	10001
18	10010
19	10011
20	10100

and as an example, for the binary, 10011, the decimal equivalent follows from:

$$(1 \times 2^4) + (0 \times 2^3) + (0 \times 2^2) + (1 \times 2^1) + (1 \times 2^0)$$

$$= 16 + 0 + 0 + 2 + 1 = 19$$

as shown above.

Negative Numbers:
So far we have considered positive numbers, both whole and fractional. Binary must also cater for negative numbers, these in the decimal system are indicated by preceding the number by a minus sign. In the binary system there can only be 0's and 1's – no other. So minus must be indicated by one of these. In perhaps the simplest method, a *sign bit* is added to the number, for example preceding the most significant bit. As an example, and generally, the sign bit is a 0 for positive numbers and a 1 for those which are negative. Where of course negative numbers do not arise, no additional bit is required. As a simple example:

89 decimal is normally 1011001 in binary

but if sign bits are required:

+89 in decimal translates to	01011001 in binary
−89 in decimal translates to	11011001 in binary

and we note that the binary for +89 has a 0 preceding the most significant digit which is not normally the case for binary, hence the 0 is classed as a *non-significant zero*.

2.2 Conversion Between Binary and Decimal

For any conversion between the two systems we will need to know the value of 2^n where the maximum value of n will be only one less than the number of digits to the left of the decimal point in the binary code. As an example, for the binary equivalent of the decimal number 6258 (1100001110010 – quoted in Sect.2.1), the maximum value of n involved is 12 (there are 13 digits). So in this case for conversion from one system to the other, the first requirement is a knowledge of the numeric value of 2^{12}. No difficulty here if there is a computer or scientific calculator nearby but in case not, Appendix 3 can be used. Let us next see how conversion can be carried out and for this we take a fairly low number otherwise the page becomes filled with brackets and calculations.

Decimal to Binary:
Take for our example the decimal number 87:

(i)   the highest power of 2 in 87 is 2^6 (= 64)
$$\therefore 87 = (1 \times 2^6) + (87 - 64) = (1 \times 2^6) + 23$$

(ii)   the highest power of 2 in 23 is 2^4 (= 16)
$$\therefore 87 = (1 \times 2^6) + (0 \times 2^5) + (1 \times 2^4) + (23 - 16 = 7)$$

[We are searching for the 0's just as much as the 1's, so the (0 $\times 2^5$) must be entered.]

(iii) the highest power of 2 in 7 is 2^2 (= 4)
$$\therefore 87 = (1 \times 2^6) + (0 \times 2^5) + (1 \times 2^4) + (0 \times 2^3) + (1 \times 2^2) + (7 - 4 = 3)$$

and clearly the 3 can be resolved as $(1 \times 2^1) + (1 \times 2^0)$.

The binary number is therefore 1010111.

Use of the "powers of 2" Table can be avoided by a "successive division by 2" method. The decimal number is continually divided by 2 and the *remainders* form the binary number, e.g. 87 divided by 2 gives 43 with a remainder of 1, this is removed from the calculation and goes into the 2^0 position in the binary number. Next 43 is divided by 2 to give 21, again with a remainder of 1 which now goes into the 2^1 position. When the number to be divided is even, there is no remainder so a 0 is generated for that particular position. The process continues until the decimal number runs out.

Binary to Decimal:
By being aware of the power index of 2 for each digit in the binary number (Sect.2.1), with help from Appendix 3 as necessary, the total decimal values for each 1 in the binary number can be added. Nothing is added where a 0 occurs. As an example:

1	0	1	0	1	1	1
:	:	:	:	:	:	:
2^6	2^5	2^4	2^3	2^2	2^1	2^0

which is equal to

$$64 + 0 + 16 + 0 + 4 + 2 + 1 = 87 .$$

2.3 Arithmetic Processes

The basic arithmetic processes used in the decimal system (addition, subtraction, etc.) are also applicable to the binary. Understanding these processes is perhaps less difficult than might be expected and confidence is given if we continually keep in mind the decimal equivalents as a check. Here again our considerations are limited to low numbers in order to avoid getting bogged down in masses of figures.

Considering addition to be the basic function in arithmetic, subtraction is then the inverse of addition. Moreover multiplication can be considered as a series of successive additions and division as the inverse of multiplication. This in fact is how computing circuits see it but it is not quite as straightforward as it first might appear so we find that we need a special section on *complements*.

2.3.1 Addition

Some simple rules are applicable first:

Adding 0 and 0 gives 0
        0 and 1 gives 1
        1 and 1 gives 0 with a *carry* of 1 into the next higher column – see below.

This is demonstrated as follows for the addition of the two binary numbers 100101 (= 37) and 10100 (= 20). This can be set out as follows:

2^5	2^4	2^3	2^2	2^1	2^0	
1	0	0	1	0	1	(= 37)
	1	0	1	0	0	(= 20)
Addition: 1	1	1	0	0	1	(= 57)

Staring with the 2^0 column, add 1×2^0 to 0×2^0, giving a digit of 1. In the 2^1 column, 0 is added to 0, giving a digit of 0. In the 2^2 column 1×2^2 is added to 1×2^2 giving 2×2^2 but we cannot have 2 as the addition because the system only allows 0 and 1. However 2×2^2 is equal to 1×2^3 hence we write 0 and carry 1 into the 2^3 column, giving in this column $0 + 0 + 1$. The 2^4 and 2^5 columns are straightforward.

Doing this electronically therefore requires that when any column is added, not only are the two numbers added together but there may also be:

(i)   a *carry-in* (C_i) to be included from the adjacent lower column;

(ii) a *carry-out* (C_o) to the adjacent higher column.

We can perhaps see this process better in action from the following table and again to avoid filling the page with 0's and 1's reasonably low numbers are used, say, adding 114 and 183. The complete process is illustrated as follows:

	2^8	2^7	2^6	2^5	2^4	2^3	2^2	2^1	2^0
Decimal number 114		0	1	1	1	0	0	1	0
Decimal number 183		1	0	1	1	0	1	1	1
Carry-in (C_i)	1	1	1	1	0	1	1	0	0
Result (297)	1	0	0	1	0	1	0	0	1
Carry-out (C_o)		1	1	1	1	0	1	1	0

(i)   Starting from the 2^0 column, $0 + 1 + 0 = 1$ in the Result line (C_i must be 0 in this case). Because 1 in the Result line is acceptable, $C_o = 0$ which becomes $C_i = 0$ in the 2^1 column.

(ii) 2^1 column: $1 + 1 + 0$ cannot equal 2 because there is no such binary value, it is therefore equal to 1 in the next higher column. Accordingly $C_o = 1$ which is also entered as $C_i = 1$ in the 2^2 column.

(iii) 2^2 column: $0 + 1 + 1 = 0$ again with $C_o = 1$, transferred as $C_i = 1$ in the 2^3 column.

The process continues up to the 2^7 column where an extra column (2^8) is required to accommodate the C_o from the 2^7 column. At this stage it is possible to visualize that a binary adder consists of a series of adding stages, one per column, with a facility for feeding into any one a carry from an adjacent one of lower significance.

Also see Section 3.5.2 for a more practical discussion on binary addition.

2.3.2 Complements

The *complement* of a binary number is simply obtained by subtracting the number from zero. Complement notation is a concept which is especially useful in the simplification of subtraction (Sect.2.3.3).

Consider an n-bit word which therefore has 2^n combinations. If we let x represent any number within the range, then x and $(2^n - x)$ are said to be complementary because $x + (2^n - x) = 2^n$. Hence $(2^n - x)$ expresses the complement of x with respect to 2^n. Let us now consider some actual figures for with these the tactics are more easily appreciated.

One's Complement:

Next consider an 8-bit word, i.e. capable of 2^8 ($= 256$) combinations and let us take any number within this range, say 109 ($= x$):

In binary	2^8 =	1	1	1	1	1	1	1	1
	x =	0	1	1	0	1	1	0	1
subtract, then complement $(2^8 - x)$	=	1	0	0	1	0	0	1	0

This complement is known as the *one's complement* because it is complementary to an "all ones" figure. Hence with respect to 2^8, 10010010 represents $-x$ and, using the sign bit method suggested in Section 2.1.2 (a 0 for positive numbers, a 1 for negative numbers – preceding the most significant digit), it is clear that this agrees with the principle because the sign digit is now a 1 and therefore the value has reversed to negative.

Also it is evident that if we wish to change any number to its negative value, all that is required is to change over the 0's and 1's. Check with any number, say decimal 93:

$+93$ = 0 1 0 1 1 1 0 1 (the first 0 signs the number as positive)

-93 = 1 0 1 0 0 0 1 0 (the first 1 now signs the number as negative)

and it is now evident that adding these two binary numbers together gives all 1's. This looks good but in fact it puts us in some difficulty because from $+93 + (-93)$ we expect to get zero, i.e. all 0's. It seems therefore that instead of zero being represented by all 0's as one might expect, it now appears a second time as all 1's when the one's complement is used. So now we have both $+0$ and -0, both equal to nothing. This is hardly desirable and is likely to create confusion. Moreover a series of 1's also results in a true binary number, e.g. 111 (= decimal 7), 1111 (= decimal 15), etc.

Two's Complement:
This has been evolved because of the complication mentioned above, it simply adds a 1 to the one's complement. By adding a 1, −0 which by the one's complement is shown as a series of 1's, becomes a series of 0's. As an example in a 4-bit system:

	1	1	1	1	which is equal to 0 in the one's complement.
Add				1	to change to the two's complement.
Resulting in	1	0	0	0	0

Note however that the technique results in a *carry* or *overflow* bit of 1. This raises an important point which is that with binary subtraction by the method of two's complement addition, the carry or overflow bit must be rejected.

Summing up therefore, the two's complement is obtained by changing over 0's and 1's and adding 1 to the result. By so doing there is no duplication of zeros and the negative values are true because any number added to its two's complement results in a true decimal 0, e.g.

+93 in binary is equal to 01011101

change over 0's and 1's and add 1 to give

−93 in binary is equal to 10100011

the addition of which gives all 0's in binary. Take another simple example:

decimal 9 = 1001,
binary two's complement = (0110 + 1) = 0111.

Hence: decimal 9 − 9 = 0, in binary, 1001 + 0111 = (1)0000 (the 1 in the result is discarded).

2.3.3 Subtraction

Binary complements are considered above in Section 2.3.2. Once the complement of a binary number has been obtained, then by *adding* it to another binary number, subtraction has taken place. This follows because the complement is the equivalent negative value.

Electronically the two's complement of a number is easily generated and it is therefore possible to follow with a binary adder for subtraction. This is a contradiction in terms so such a device is known as an *adder/subtracter*. Here is a simple example showing how such a circuit might calculate 33 − 27:

33		0	0	1	0	0	0	0	1
− 27		1	1	1	0	0	1	0	1 add

(1) 0 0 0 0 0 1 1 0 = 6

(the bracketed 1 is rejected).

Next a second example so that we can get used to the method. Subtract decimal 147 from 173 in binary:

First find the complement of 147:

147 in binary is	10010011	(Appendix 4)
Its complement is	01101100 + 1 =	01101101

Adding:

173		1	0	1	0	1	1	0	1
Complement 147		0	1	1	0	1	1	0	1

(1) 0 0 0 1 1 0 1 0

which as the Appendix shows is equal to 26. Note again that the 1 on the left is discarded. The two's complement method is an ingenious system because electronic circuits easily identify and change over 1's for 0's and vice versa. After this the standard binary adder takes over.

2.3.4. Multiplication

Multiplication in binary is performed by a technique of shifting and then adding, in fact not unlike the multiplication process learned at school. With binary it so happens that the process is quite undemanding because we have no need of multiplication tables. However, with binary (as we might have guessed) there is much more of it. Two definitions first:

multiplicand – the quantity to be multiplied,

multiplier – the quantity by which a multiplicand is multiplied.

Consider the multiplication of decimal 23 by 10 in binary. Note that each time a shift to the left occurs, this is equivalent to multiplying by 2.

$$2^7 \ 2^6 \ 2^5 \ 2^4 \ 2^3 \ 2^2 \ 2^1 \ 2^0$$

			1	0	1	1	1	(23 – multiplicand)
				1	0	1	0	(10 – multiplier)

```
            0 0 0 0 0   (the 2⁰ value in the multiplier is 0
                         – add nothing)

          1 0 1 1 1     (the 2¹ value in the multiplier is 1
                         – shift multiplicand one place to
                         the left)

        0 0 0 0 0       (the 2² value in the multiplier is 0
                         – shift to left and add nothing)

      1 0 1 1 1         (the 2³ value in the multiplier is 1
                         – shift multiplicand one place to
                         the left)
```

2^0 value in the multiplier is 0 – add nothing)

2^1 value in the multiplier is 1 – shift multiplicand one place to the left)

2^2 value in the multiplier is 0 – shift to left and add nothing)

2^3 value in the multiplier is 1 – shift multiplicand one place to the left)

1 1 1 0 0 1 1 0   Result

which Appendix 4 shows to be equivalent to a decimal value of 230.

Looking back on what we have done, the first and third moves add 0 to the result but create the necessary shift (not required on first move). The second and fourth moves are effective in the multiplication process and are equivalent to multiplying by 2 and 8 (three shifts, each × 2) respectively, the results when added together effectively multiplying by 10.

2.3.5 Division

As with binary multiplication, binary division is somewhat simpler than the equivalent decimal operation. It follows the technique of multiplication but in reverse. Three definitions first:

divisor – the number by which another number is divided;

dividend – the number which is divided by the divisor;

quotient – is the result given by dividing one quantity by another.

In operation the divisor is repeatedly subtracted from the dividend with shifts as appropriate. Here is an uncomplicated example:

Divide 60 by 10 in binary:

Dividend: 111100   (60) – Appendix 4

Divisor: 1010   (10)

```
              1 1 0      – quotient
            ─────────
1 0 1 0 ) 1 1 1 1 0 0
          1 0 1 0 : :    – divisor
          ─────────
            1 0 1 0 :
            1 0 1 0 :    – divisor shifted to right
            ─────────
            0 0 0 0 0
```

The quotient as shown above is therefore 110 (decimal 6).

The basic procedure is:

(1) compare the divisor with the left-hand bits of the dividend

(2)   should the divisor be greater, then quotient = 0. Shift divisor one place to the right

(3)   attempt subtraction again. If not possible, then (2). If divisor less than dividend then quotient = 1. Shift divisor one place to the right.

The above is an example of a division with no remainder, e.g. 10 goes into 60 exactly. Next is another binary subtraction but now resulting in a remainder.

Divide 50 by 8 in binary:

Dividend: 110010   (50)

Divisor: 1000   (8)

```
                  1 1 0
                _____
      1 0 0 0 ) 1 1 0 0 1 0
               1 0 0 0 : :
               _____
               1 0 0 1 :
               1 0 0 0 :   – shift divisor to right
               _____
               0 0 0 1 0   – remainder
```

Hence quotient = 110 (decimal 6) and Remainder = 010 (decimal 2).

Things can get a little more complicated than this but basically this is how it is done.

Chapter 3

ELECTRONIC LOGIC

We can consider the term *logic* when applied to digital technology as meaning the arrangement of digital elements to perform a specified task. Let us first illustrate this in a simple way, thereby gaining an introduction to the techniques by which we can illustrate on paper the action of any switching system no matter how complicated it may be. Below is an analysis by which the operation of an uncomplicated digital switching system can be completely described.

At home we may have lighting on our stairs controlled by two switches, one at the bottom, the other at the top. Going up we switch on the stair light when we are at the bottom of the stairs and are able to switch it off when we reach the top. Going down, the same switch at the top now switches the light on, switched off again when we reach the bottom. The switches are known as two-way and are shown in the complete circuit in Figure 3.1. Here is the *truth table* for the circuit:

Top switch	Bottom switch	Lamp
1	0	0
1	1	1
0	1	0
0	0	1

A truth table is therefore a list of the various operations or combinations possible in a particular logic system, indicating the truth or otherwise of each move. Truth tables therefore facilitate the design of complex switching systems. In this example we equate digital 1 with ON, digital 0 with OFF. We will meet several more truth tables as we progress.

3.1 The Basic Logic Functions
Boolean algebra is a system which combines mathematics with logic in that symbols are used to represent the structure of

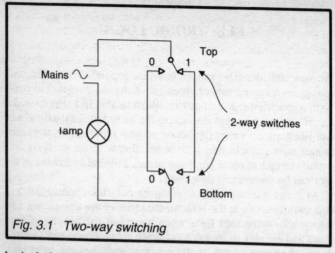

Fig. 3.1 Two-way switching

logical thought. Boole's work has been adapted for digital systems and generally for these the basic symbols we use are 1 for *true* and 0 for *false*. The basic functions used in circuit analysis are AND, OR and NOT. There are others but these can be considered as extensions of the basic ones. Let us introduce them by means of a well-known family problem.

A little boy is caught in the garden with a hose in his hand (A) and running away is the family cat, soaking wet (B). We now have two sets of input data from which reasoning or logic can come to only one conclusion (F), he did it. Here A and B on their own do not allow the conclusion F but together the guilt is proved. The boy and cat irregularity is expressed as <u>A AND B = F</u>, i.e. given both facts A and B together, the conclusion F can be reached. Note that the AND is in capital letters, it is a logical manipulation indicating that both incidents must happen together for there to be a result. In Boolean algebra shorthand, A AND B is reduced to A.B, i.e. the AND operator is represented by a full stop. In our everyday mathematics the full stop may be used as a sign of multiplication, Boolean algebra uses it in a completely different way.

Equally there are occasions when two or more facts need not be present together (as for the AND condition above) for a valid conclusion to be drawn. Typically a single switch (A) and lamp

(B) can be used as an illustration. We can look at the switch to determine whether the lamp is on (F) or equally we can look at the lamp itself. Either switch or lamp indicates the on or off condition and it is not necessary that both should be observed together. This is expressed as $\underline{A\ OR\ B = F}$. The OR is generally represented by the + sign, again having no relationship with our normal mathematical "plus".

The NOT function is simplicity itself. It merely reverses the logic condition, e.g. if A = 1, then NOT A = 0, similarly if A = 0, then NOT A = 1. The NOT function is indicated by the addition of a bar so that NOT A is written as $\overline{A}$.

We examine electronic gates based on these functions in the following Sections. Note that here a *gate* is an electrical circuit with a single output controlled by one or more input signals, i.e. the gate is open or closed by what is happening at its input. Let us not gloss over this Chapter on the assumption that gates are an unimportant feature in digital technology. It is very much the opposite and in fact we will find that there can be many thousands of them coupled together in a single integrated circuit. Generally the movement of digital information relies on the operation of the digital gate.

3.1.1 The AND Gate
The simplest AND gate has two inputs only and both must be at logic 1 for the output to go to 1. Figure 3.2(i) shows how this function can be achieved by using two electromagnetic switches or "relays", each with a single "make" contact and with the two contacts connected in series. The relay coil inputs are marked x and y and both relays must therefore be energised for current to flow through the two contacts to the output terminal marked f. In more detail a voltage applied only to input terminal x operates relay A but this has no effect on the output f which therefore remains at logic 0, neither does it have any effect on the output if relay B on its own is operated. But when both relays A AND B are operated, +5 V (the logic 1) appears at f.

A simple diode AND gate is shown at (ii), this has three inputs and demonstrates that any number of inputs can be accommodated. When any input logic signal is at 0 (i.e. equivalent to connecting the input terminal to the 0 V line), current

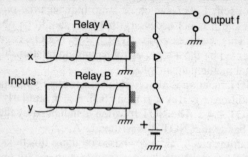

(i) Electromagnetic relay circuit for 2-input gate

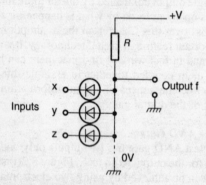

(ii) A 3-input diode gate circuit

Inputs		Output
x	y	f
0	0	0
0	1	0
1	0	0
1	1	1

(iii) Truth table for a 2-input gate

(iv) Symbols

Fig. 3.2 The AND gate

flows through that particular diode, maintaining it at low resistance. This creates a voltage drop across R sufficient to keep the output terminal f near 0 V. The current through R is reinforced if more than one or all inputs are at logic 0. Only when all the input logic signals are at 1 are all diodes in the high resistance state for then the potentials on both sides of them are equal. The current through R is then cut off with the potential at f rising to +V, i.e. logic 1. Note that here f goes positive in switching to 1 so we are demonstrating *positive logic* (Sect.1.4.3).

The truth table for a two-input AND gate is shown in the figure at (iii) and at (iv) are the two main symbols in use. The logical equation for a 3-input AND gate is therefore:

$$f = x \cdot y \cdot z$$

(and we recall that the full stops indicate the AND function). This equation therefore indicates that f goes to 1 only when x, y, and z (and any additional inputs) are all at 1. This circuit is said to belong to the family of *Diode-Resistance Logic* (DRL) since these are the two types of component used.

3.1.2 The OR Gate

Whereas with the simple AND gate both inputs must be at logic 1 for there to be an output of 1, with the OR gate any input on its own going to 1 produces an output of 1. This is shown by the truth table in Figure 3.3(iii). In (i) of this figure is the electromagnetic switch illustration and at (ii) is the simple diode circuit for a 3-input gate. When any input goes positive to logic 1 therefore, its diode conducts and provides a through path for that potential to reach f.

The diode OR gate is slightly less complicated compared with the AND gate because no power supply is needed, however what little power is consumed must be supplied by the input signal. This confirms that with logic 0 at all the input terminals, the output f must be at 0 because no voltage exists anywhere.

The logical equation for a 3-input OR gate is therefore:

$$f = x + y + z$$

(and we recall that the + sign indicates the OR function). Again

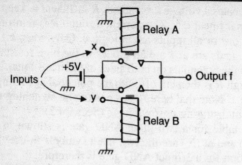

(i) Electromagnetic relay circuit for 2-input OR gate

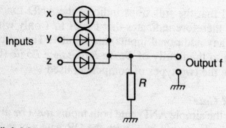

(ii) A 3-input diode gate circuit

Inputs		Output
x	y	f
0	0	0
0	1	1
1	0	1
1	1	1

(iii) Truth table for a 2-input gate

American Military Standard (MS)

British Standard (BS)

(iv) Symbols

Fig. 3.3 The OR gate

the circuit in (ii) is said to belong to the family of *Diode-Resistance Logic.*

3.1.3 The NOT Gate

This is the least complicated of all gates, also known as an *invertor.* There are only two conditions in binary digital, 0 and 1 hence when a NOT gate has an input of logic 0, its output must be at logic 1 and vice versa. This is also known as *complementing.* As shown earlier the function is indicated by the addition of a horizontal bar, i.e. NOT x is written $\overline{x}$ and the truth table, although perhaps obvious, is shown in Figure 3.4(iii).

Such a function is easily obtained by use of a single relay as shown in Figure 3.4(i). When there is no input, i.e. $x = 0$, then the normally made contacts of the relay provide a 5 V potential to the output terminal, i.e. $f = 1$. When the relay is operated by an input of 1, the output is disconnected, i.e. $f = 0$.

A practical single NOT gate is shown at (ii). It is an elementary circuit unlikely to be used in integrated circuit form because of its requirement of resistors, nevertheless it demonstrates a practical method. A transistor is suitable because it is an *inverting amplifier* when connected in common-emitter. With 0 V input to the base, only a very small collector current flows, the voltage drop across R being correspondingly small, hence f is approximately at the supply line potential. Conversely for a 1 input to the base, the collector current rises sufficiently for the voltage drop across R to be such that f is virtually at 0 V.

The symbols used are shown at (iv) of the Figure. Indication of a NOT function is made by adding a small circle to a symbol, the circle can be at the input or the output as required. An example of the use of a NOT gate is given in (v) of the figure which shows an AND gate with one NOT gate at its z input, hence:

$$f = x \cdot y \cdot \overline{z}$$

meaning that f goes to logic 1 only when x and y are at logic 1 and z is at 0. This particular logic diagram can be reduced to that shown where the inversion circle is now at the input of the AND gate.

41

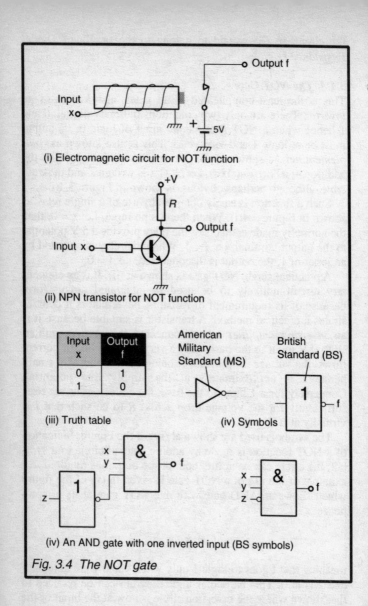

(i) Electromagnetic circuit for NOT function

(ii) NPN transistor for NOT function

Input x	Output f
0	1
1	0

(iii) Truth table

(iv) Symbols

American Military Standard (MS)

British Standard (BS)

(iv) An AND gate with one inverted input (BS symbols)

Fig. 3.4 The NOT gate

3.1.4 NAND and NOR

These follow directly from the AND, OR and NOT gates and in fact they are simply mixtures of them, i.e. NOT AND and NOT OR. Theoretically NAND and NOR are equivalent to AND and OR gates followed by invertors. The truth table for a NAND gate is therefore the same as that for an AND gate except that each f value is inverted and similarly for the NOR gate. The tables are given in Figure 3.5(i). This inversion is also shown by the logic symbols in Figure 3.5(ii). We see that the symbols are the same as for AND and OR except for the addition of the inversion circle at the output (this also applies for the MS symbols). Accordingly for a 3-input gate:

$$\text{NAND} \ \ f = \overline{x \cdot y \cdot z} \qquad \text{NOR} \ \ f = \overline{x + y + z}$$

NAND and NOR gates are especially useful in integrated circuit design. Both can be so connected as to provide the truth tables of each of the other gates and many advantages accrue from using one type only of a gate in a system.

NAND

Inputs		Output
x	y	f
0	0	1
0	1	1
1	0	1
1	1	0

NOR

Inputs		Output
x	y	f
0	0	1
0	1	0
1	0	0
1	1	0

(i) Truth tables

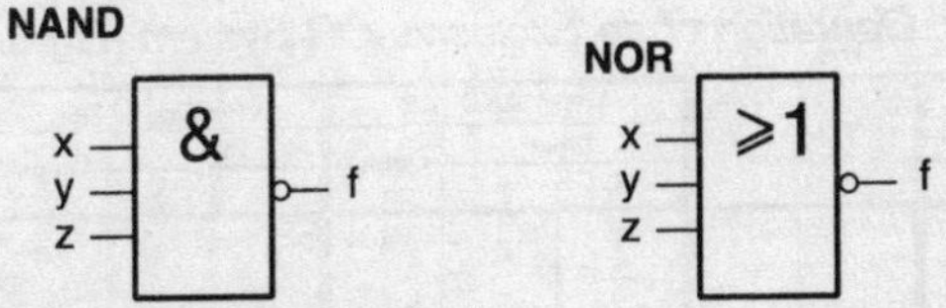

NAND

NOR

(ii) Symbols (British Standard)

Fig. 3.5 NAND and NOR gates

43

3.1.5 Exclusive-OR

This has the same truth table as the OR gate {Fig.3.3(iii)} except that when the two inputs are both at 1, the output remains at 0 as shown in the truth table in Figure 3.6(i). This type of gate is restricted to two inputs only. The exclusive-OR function has its own special algebraic symbol $\oplus$, hence:

$$f = x \oplus y$$

We can gain an insight into the analysis of logic networks by using a *minimization* process in which a seemingly complex system of elementary gates (AND, OR, NOT) is reduced to a single gate; in this case, the exclusive-OR.

From the truth table, f changes to 1 when:

OR
    (i) $x = 0$, $y = 1$ or equally, $\overline{x} = 1$, $y = 1$

    (ii) $x = 1$, $y = 0$ or equally, $x = 1$, $\overline{y} = 1$

so the complete expression for the exclusive-OR is:

$$f = \overline{x} \cdot y + x \cdot \overline{y}$$

i.e. when this expression is satisfied, $f = 1$.

The horizontal bars indicate that two NOT gates are required. The two full stops call for AND gates and the + sign requires an OR gate. A suitable arrangement is shown in Figure 3.6(ii) where $\overline{x} \cdot y$ is produced at the output of the upper AND gate and $x \cdot \overline{y}$ at the lower. Both are then applied to the single OR gate. The complete operation is developed in Table 3.1.

The logic symbols for the exclusive-OR gate are given in (iii) of the figure.

Table 3.1 *Operation of an Exclusive-OR System (Fig.3.6(ii))*

Inputs		$\overline{x}$	$\overline{y}$	Upper AND gate			Lower AND gate			System Output
				Input		Output	Input		Output	
x	y			$\overline{x}$	y		x	$\overline{y}$		f
0	0	1	1	1	0	0	0	1	0	0
0	1	1	0	1	1	1	0	0	0	1
1	0	0	1	0	0	0	1	1	1	1
1	1	0	0	0	1	0	1	0	0	0

44

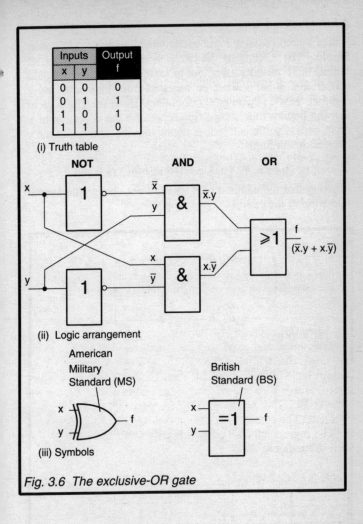

Inputs		Output
x	y	f
0	0	0
0	1	1
1	0	1
1	1	0

(i) Truth table

(ii) Logic arrangement

American
Military
Standard (MS)

British
Standard (BS)

(iii) Symbols

Fig. 3.6 The exclusive-OR gate

3.2 The Laws and Theorems of Logic

From the above it is clear that the flow of digital information can be controlled by a system of electronic gates and it is also clear that to design a circuit having a large number of gates when a smaller number may be just as effective, is wasteful and certainly not good engineering practice. This can be demonstrated by representing logic operations by relay switches as in Figure 3.7(i). Clearly as the circuit is drawn, the output is at logical 0. To produce an output of logical 1 therefore it would appear that either x must be operated (top line) or x and y together must be operated (bottom line). However it is evident that the bottom line is superfluous because the operation of x on its own is sufficient, it does not require the addition of the y contact. Accordingly:

$$x + x \cdot y \equiv x \quad \{\text{i.e. } x \text{ OR } (x \text{ AND } y) \equiv x\}$$

showing that the addition of x . y does not change the logical operation of the circuit.

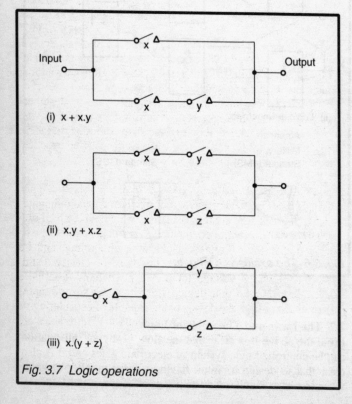

(i) x + x.y

(ii) x.y + x.z

(iii) x.(y + z)

Fig. 3.7 Logic operations

Of course, this result is obvious even on a casual examination of the circuit, but let us be under no illusions, most switching circuits are not so easily resolved, in fact specialized techniques are usually required.

Another simple example is given at (ii) in the figure. Here the equivalent circuit is obtained in Boolean algebra:

$$x \cdot y + x \cdot z \equiv x \cdot (y + z)$$

stating that x AND y together OR x AND z together switch the circuit through. However the circuit can be simplified as shown after the equals sign to:

$$x \text{ AND } (y \text{ OR } z)$$

the result being that one relay contact can now be omitted as shown in (iii) of the figure yet exactly the same facilities are provided.

There are many basic laws and theorems in Boolean algebra, the various laws may be used firstly to disentangle complicated expressions while the theorems enable complex switching arrangements to be reduced to the simplest possible.

These laws and theorems are essential for use by designers of digital systems and integrated circuits but are not for us who are unlikely to be called upon in the design operation, in fact to plod through the whole of Boolean algebra with no practical finality may be more than a little wearisome.

3.3 Logic Circuits

So far in this Chapter we have outlined the various logic gates in general use. These are the basic units which make up all digital systems. As a reminder, generally all signals can be classified as 0 or 1 where 0 represents a low or zero voltage and 1 a higher voltage, say 3–5 volts and this must be clearly distinguishable from the voltage for 0. We might now describe a logic gate as an electronic device which can have several inputs but only one output, the device being capable of considering its inputs and making a decision as to the output. Truth tables are used to show the output condition of a gate for all possible input values.

Logic circuits are with us today in so many different applications that it is impossible to list them all. At home we have electronic calculators, clocks and watches, childrens' toys, kitchen equipment, television and radio sets. In the office is the inevitable computer and other office machinery while outside is the car with its processor-controlled engine. In all these and all others, logic gates make decisions based on the information transmitted to them. We see little or nothing of these logic gates because most are enclosed in integrated circuit packages, themselves so reduced in size by modern technology as to be almost invisible.

Figures 3.2 to 3.4 show simple circuits which provide AND, OR and NOT facilities. The circuits shown in Figures 3.2(ii) and 3.3(ii) are classed as *diode–resistor logic* (DRL) for obvious reasons. Figure 3.4(ii) for the NOT function gives an example of *resistor–transistor logic* (RTL). These are known as *logic families* and were the first to arrive and although systems may be designed around individual resistors, diodes and transistors, because most digital circuits are contained within integrated circuit packages, they belong to logic families which are especially suited to such packaging. Two important families are known as *transistor–transistor logic* (TTL) and *metal-oxide–semiconductor logic* (MOS). These are described in the following sections, other families exist just as important, but we choose these because they are used in quantity and also they introduce us to both bipolar and field-effect transistor (uni-polar) systems.

3.3.1 Transistor–Transistor Logic (TTL)

TTL was the earliest integrated circuit logic family to be developed for use in large quantities. Normally it works at a nominal 5 V and embodies bipolar junction transistors. As mentioned in Section 3.1.4, NAND gates are especially useful in integrated circuits because of their flexibility, here therefore we consider a TTL NAND gate as used in integrated circuit production.

For this the input circuit is built around a *multi-emitter transistor*, marked $T1$ in Figure 3.8 which shows a simplified TTL NAND gate – in this particular case all the transistors are n-p-n type. In manufacture it is possible to diffuse several separate emitters into a single base region and in Figure 3.8 $T1$ is shown as having three. The truth table for a NAND gate is shown in Figure 3.5 which shows that when any input line (in

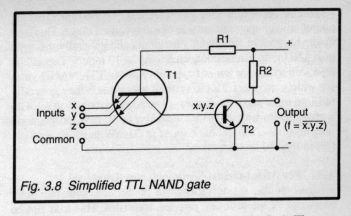

Fig. 3.8 Simplified TTL NAND gate

this case x or y) is at logic 0, the output is at logic 1. The output only changes to logic 0 when *both* x and y are at 1. An approximate idea of the actual voltage levels used in a 5 V system is given in Section 1.4.3.

The positive bias applied to the base of $T1$ is such that if all inputs and therefore emitters are at 'high' positive potential, the base-emitter junctions are not forward biased, hence the collector is nearly at the supply voltage, so biasing $T2$ 'on'. The voltage drop across $R2$ causes the output to be at 'low'. Connection of any of the emitters to the 0 V (common) rail forward-biases the base-emitter junction of $T1$, the collector voltage falls and $T2$ cuts off, that is, the output terminal switches to 'high'. This process clearly agrees with the truth table.

To keep the explanation simple, a further pair of transistors and a diode have been omitted. These would normally be connected to the output terminals, not to change the overall NAND operation in any way but mainly to increase the speed of switching.

What may be difficult to appreciate perhaps, especially for readers who have dabbled in transistor circuit construction, is that circuits such as in Figure 3.8 (plus the additional components mentioned above) can be packed in large numbers into integrated circuits. This is just a single example, all logic gates are obtained in integrated circuit form using TTL.

Gates such as this may feed into other gate circuits and it is evident that if the output terminal is connected in parallel to several inputs of following gates, there is the possibility that the output voltage may fall outside of the specified range. This limits the number of following gate inputs and generally this type of NAND gate can be connected to up to 10 inputs. The gate is then said to have a *fan-out* capability of 10. TTL NAND gates are widely used in IC logic systems and as such they generally fall into three separate classes – *low power* (about 1 mW) with a propagation time of 30 ns; *standard* at 10 mW, propagation time around 12ns; and *high speed* at 20 mW but with a propagation time of less than 6 ns.

3.3.2 The Metal-Oxide–Semiconductor Transistor

Without doubt, most readers are conversant with the inner workings of the ordinary junction transistor. This may not be the case for field-effect transistors so we have a brief look at the general principles of these first and anyway a little revision never comes amiss. The field-effect transistor is classed as unipolar because its current path is not through both p and n materials as for the standard bipolar transistor, but wholly in one. The substrate may be of either p or n material. Figure 3.9(i) shows an f.e.t. diagrammatically and in this case the channel (source to drain) is n-type. Accordingly this particular type is known as *n-channel* and the reason for the term "channel" will be evident from the figure.

Here we describe the operation of an n-channel device in which current flow is along a bar of n-type semiconductor material from *source* to *drain* under normal conduction principles. The free electrons are obtained from donor impurity atoms and these are repelled from the source and attracted towards the drain because of the applied potentials. However the p-type *gate* electrodes form p-n junctions as shown and associated with these are *depletion layers*. Since the d.c. potential along the bar rises positively from source to drain, the depletion layers are not of constant width but increase on the drain side because the potential between p and n is greater there.

The Figure shows that the p-n junctions are reverse-biased and because the width of the depletion layer varies with the magnitude of the bias, as V_{gs} becomes more negative, the width of the channel and therefore electron flow decrease. The resis-

50

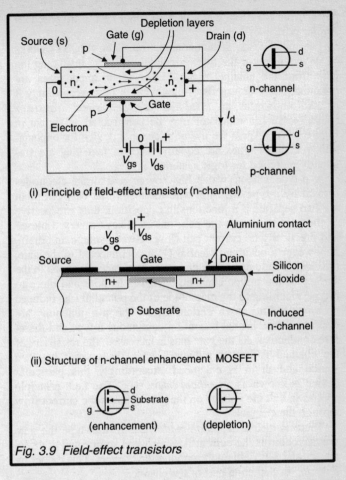

(i) Principle of field-effect transistor (n-channel)

(ii) Structure of n-channel enhancement MOSFET

(enhancement) (depletion)

Fig. 3.9 Field-effect transistors

tance of the device therefore increases hence the drain current I_d falls as the negative potential V_{gs} increases. Thus as with a bipolar transistor, a relatively large current is dominated by a small voltage. However there is one important difference, here the control is by application of an electric *field*. Fields are set up by extremely small currents, hence the gate input resistance is very high (even up to thousands of megohms), a property so useful when a device such as a gate must absorb practically no power from the driving circuit. P-channel f.e.t.'s are based on similar principles.

The metal-oxide–semiconductor transistor (MOST) works on an extension of the f.e.t. principle in that by insulating the gate from the channel, even higher input impedances are obtained, many thousands of megohms in fact. Accordingly it is also known as an *insulated-gate field-effect transistor* (IGFET). Such a transistor may be constructed as shown in Figure 3.9(ii). Again we use an n-channel device for explanation, p-channel types are equally used, in fact they are frequently preferred for logic systems.

A p-type silicon wafer has source and drain electrodes formed by n-type diffusion with the result that between them are two separate p-n junctions in opposition, thus irrespective of the polarity across the pair, one is always reversed biased and practically no current can flow between source and drain. If however a positive potential (V_{gs}) is connected to the gate, the electric field due to the charge on it attracts electrons to the surface of the p-type channel, changing it more and more to n-type according to the magnitude of the potential (the induced n-channel). Thus to a certain extent the p-n junctions are destroyed, the channel becoming continuous n-type and therefore conductive. As the gate bias is increased, the resistivity of the channel is further reduced, hence the current between source and drain is enhanced. Accordingly this particular device is known as an *enhancement* type. The f.e.t. principle applies in that the voltage on the gate controls the current flow through the channel.

There is also a *depletion-mode* f.e.t. In this type the gate voltage controls the current flow between source and drain by the action of its field on the conducting channel. This it does by reducing or depleting part of the channel.

Figure 3.9(ii) shows an induced n-channel type but opposite polarities are also used, especially in CMOS (Complementary Metal-oxide–Semiconductor) where one n-channel transistor is paired with one p-channel transistor to provide special facilities in switching circuits and especially for digital gates.

3.3.3 Metal-oxide–Semiconductor Logic
Both p-channel and n-channel field-effect transistors are

employed in MOS technology. When used separately they become PMOS and NMOS or used together, CMOS. MOS logic has the advantage of high packing density in an integrated circuit, this is coupled with low power requirements. In fact CMOS circuits can operate as quickly as TTL yet consume less power.

Both PMOS and NMOS transistors can be adapted for use as resistors. For this the gate is connected to the drain so that the transistor conducts. The value of resistance obtained therefore depends on the cross-section of the channel. Using this method, standard MOS transistors within an integrated circuit can be used, so simplifying the manufacturing process.

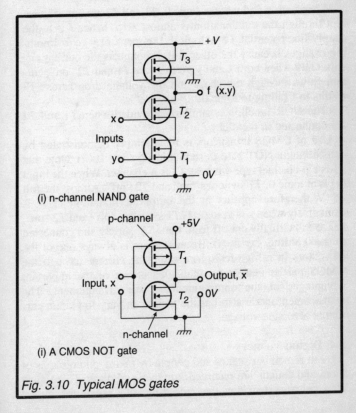

(i) n-channel NAND gate

(i) A CMOS NOT gate

Fig. 3.10 Typical MOS gates

We take as an example the n-channel enhancement mode MOS transistor (NMOS), one which is widely used in logic systems. Figure 3.10(i) shows a MOS NAND gate suitable for inclusion in an integrated circuit. Note that it contains similar MOS transistors only, it is therefore suitable for LSI (Large-Scale Integration – having more than 100 gates in a single IC package). The suitability is increased by the fact that as the Figure shows, similar electrodes belonging to different transistors are connected together in which case one region only is required in the fabrication process. The figure shows a two-input gate. A resistive load is required and this is conveniently provided by $T3$ acting solely as a resistance as explained above (gate connected to drain).

When both x and y are at logic 0, $T1$ and $T2$ are cut off, current through the combination is almost zero, hence f is at the supply-line potential, i.e. at logic 1. If either x or y go to 1 nothing changes because the other still disconnects the current circuit. Only when both x and y go to 1, are $T1$ and $T2$ "on", current flows through the chain and the voltage drop across $T3$ results in f falling to logic 0.

(The NOR function is similarly provided when $T1$ and $T2$ are connected in parallel.)

Use of CMOS transistors is most simply demonstrated by considering a NOT gate as shown in Figure 3.10(ii). Note that $T1$ is a p-channel type whereas $T2$ is n-channel. When the input (x) is at logic 0, $T1$ switches "on" and $T2$ "off". Almost the full +5 V therefore appears at the output terminal, i.e. f = 1. Conversely when x is at logic 1, $T1$ switches "off" and $T2$ "on", hence f is virtually cut off from the +5 V supply and connected to the 0 V line, i.e. f = 0. Because there is always one of the transistors in a high-resistance state, the current through the CMOS pair is extremely small, this is one of the important advantages of the complementary pair arrangement. The enhancement mode also has the facility of very low drain current at zero gate voltage.

3.4 Digital Memory

We can remember scenes and people by taking photographs of them and sounds are recorded on tapes and discs. There must also be a system for the recording and regain of digital information and this is aptly described as the *memory*. Very little in the digital world functions without some sort of memory. Memory elements are therefore electronic circuits which store digital information and release it as required. Although digital computers and word processors make extensive use of memory elements, memory circuits have crept into so many other digital systems that they are too numerous to list. Generally a memory element resembles or is a number of gates as already described, usually connected so that the information which is fed in is retained after the input signal ceases. The information can then be read or erased as required. Memory in this form is a requirement only of digital systems, it cannot be used for analogue which has its own techniques.

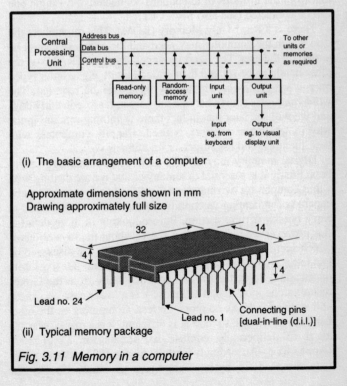

(i) The basic arrangement of a computer

(ii) Typical memory package

Fig. 3.11 Memory in a computer

As an introduction we might usefully first look at the organization of a computer to see the different kinds of memory used, this is illustrated in a simple way in Figure 3.11(i). The Central Processing Unit (CPU) is the heart of the machine and just like us, a brain needs a memory to go with it – it is hardly possible to work on a problem if we cannot remember what it is!

The *Address Bus* may need some explanation. *Bus* is a shortened form of *busbar*, until the computer came along, denoting a system of conductors carrying electrical power. To call in the information and instructions necessary for processing and to deliver the answers the CPU must be able to address the right memory locations. We might compare this with a telephone system in which every user has a discrete number or code so that from the millions of telephones connected, any single one can be contacted (see also Sect.3.4.1).

There is a Read-Only Memory (ROM). This remembers the data which the computer may need and this memory cannot be erased by the user. The Random Access Memory (RAM) on the other hand can be set and then erased at will, e.g. a letter typed on a word-processor which may no longer be required. The word *random* is somewhat of a misnomer, it arose in early days and we will see later that in fact there is nothing random in the way in which the memory is used. Happily computers with their memories do not forget as we humans do.

Digital memory may involve us in some rather large numbers. Firstly it is essential to remember that we are dealing with a unit comprising two states only, referred to as 0 and 1. A cell capable of indicating its condition (i.e. set as 0 or 1) is said to carry one bit of information. Before looking in more detail at this however we ought to clear the air about the mysterious K which seems to crop up whenever computers are discussed. K is a letter which has been steadily creeping into our lives with metrication. Short for *kilo*, it came originally from the Greek, meaning one thousand. The metric k is a lower case one and it still stands for 1000, no more, no less. Computers on the other hand are not metric so their K is different, it is a capital one and as if to deliberately confuse us, stands for 2^{10} or 1024 (Appendix 3). Accordingly a *kilobit* means 1024 bits and a *kilobyte* means 1024 bytes, eight times as much. Usually the capacity of a block of memory is quoted as 16K, 64K, etc., in which case the K usually refers to kilobytes. A 16K memory can therefore store 16×1024 bytes, i.e. it comprises $16 \times 1024 \times 8$ individual memory cells.

Larger capacities still are rated in *megabits* or more usually, in *megabytes*. Mega is from the Greek for "great" which in metrication means 1 000 000 but for computers, 2^{20}, i.e. 1 048 576 so a memory capacity quoted as 1M usually indicates this number of *bytes*. Clearly whether the K and M refer to bits or bytes should always be stated but in our casual way this is often omitted and as indicated above, the reference is normally to *bytes*. Accordingly:

8 cells together = 8 bits, normally classed as 1 byte (2^3 bits)

1024 bits (2^{10})	= 1 kilobit
1024 bytes (8 kilobits)	= 1 kilobyte
1,048,576 (2^{20} bits)	= 1 Megabit
1,048,576 bytes (2^{23} bits)	= 1 Megabyte

There are also the Gigabit and Gigabyte for extremely large memories (Giga = 10^9).

Thus we see that although the prefixes have been borrowed from the metric system, there is very little metric about computers. There is no need to remember the actual numbers involved, but simply that 1 byte = 8 bits, kilo multiplies by 2^{10} and Mega by 2^{20}, everything naturally in powers of 2. For a rough assessment however, note that the computer kilo and Mega are only slightly higher than the metric ones, for example in round figures 8 kilobits can be thought of as just over 8000 bits.

Read-Only Memory – it is evident that some instructions such as the individual steps to be taken for addition, subtraction, square roots, etc., never change and once put into the system must not be lost (loss can happen with some types of memory when the power is switched off). The bit patterns forming the instructions and constants (e.g. the value of π) are written into a ROM once only, thereafter reference can be made to these at any time, they are never changed, hence the term "read-only".

ROM's are generally available manufactured by both bipolar and MOS technology. Usually the bipolar is used where a greater speed of operation is required. Typical single IC packages at present have storage capacities ranging from about 1 kilobit to more than a million bits with physical dimensions of the order of those shown in Figure 3.11(ii). The pins (24 in this case) fit into sockets on the system base-board.

Random-Access Memory – data can be both written in and read out of this type of memory and any one of the total number of locations can be addressed at any time. It is mostly used for storing programs with the associated data and for gathering the results. As distinct from ROM, switching off the power may lose the information because all memory cells restore to logic 0. RAM's can be subdivided into two distinct classes:

(i) *static* – switchable into either of its two states in which it then remains. It can then be read any number of times until a reset pulse is applied;

(ii) *dynamic* – generally this type relies on the capacitance effects in a solid-state device, e.g. a logic 1 might be considered to be stored when the capacitance is charged. Since the charge decays, it has to be refreshed periodically on a *refresh cycle*. Generally MOST transistors are used (Sect.3.3.2), the electrical charge being extremely small, of some $10^{-14} - 10^{-16}$ coulombs. The refreshing circuitry is frequently built into the integrated circuit along with the memory cells.

We might define the *access time* for a particular type of memory as the time taken to locate and transfer an item of data in the memory. Semiconductor storage memories such as the ROM's and RAM'S described above have considerably shorter access times compared with discs, magnetic tapes and bubble memories (these are considered later). As an example, MOSFET RAM'S may have access times from 100 ns up to 1 µs. Bipolar RAM's have even lower access times.

3.4.1 Addressing Memory

A memory cell is of course useless unless it can be found quickly so as we have seen above its address must be immediately available. Section 2.1.1 shows that the number of discrete codes available to a string of n binary digits is 2^n and this indicates that the address bus, far from being a single line as in Figure 3.11, must contain n wires. A small microcomputer may have an address bus consisting of 15 or 16 such wires, hence catering for 2^{15} (32,768) or 2^{16} (65,536) separate memory locations. Higher memory capacities require 32-bit addressing.

The internal memory of a computer might be arranged as in Figure 3.12 which in effect is an expansion of Figure 3.11(i). Here we consider a small read-only package having 1024 locations, each of 8 bits. To address such a number of locations a binary code 10 bits long is required (2^{10} = 1024), hence the Read-Only Memory integrated circuit has 10 address inputs which we have labelled $A_0 - A_9$. For the Random-Access Memory with only 256 locations, 8 address inputs only are required, $A_0 - A_7$. Note that the units are connected to the same address bus, there is no confusion however for if one unit is using the bus, the others are prevented from so doing because their CS terminals (*Chip Select* – an integrated circuit is often called a "chip") are not energized. As an example, when a particular CS is connected to logic 1, that unit can be accessed, the other units remain with CS at logic 0, making them ineffective. The Address Bus is therefore available to only one unit at a time.

Here is a single example of the use not only of the Address Bus but also of the Data Bus. Suppose the CPU has to read the data stored in location 200 in the Random-Access Memory, it accordingly puts the following digital code onto the address bus.

$$A_{15}\ A_{14} \qquad\qquad A_7 \qquad\qquad A_0$$
$$0\ 1\ 0\ 0\ 0\ 0\ 0\ 0\ 1\ 1\ 0\ 0\ 1\ 0\ 0\ 0$$

(Note the large number of digits required to read one memory location, yet this is accomplished in practically no time at all by a processor.)

From Figure 3.12 we see that bits A_7 to A_0 representing the location 200 (see Appendix 4) are applied to both memory units. However bit A_{14} is at logic 1 and this is applied only to the Random-Access Memory hence this is the only unit which becomes operative. It therefore reads out onto the Data Bus at terminals D_0 to D_7 the contents of its location 200. As shown in

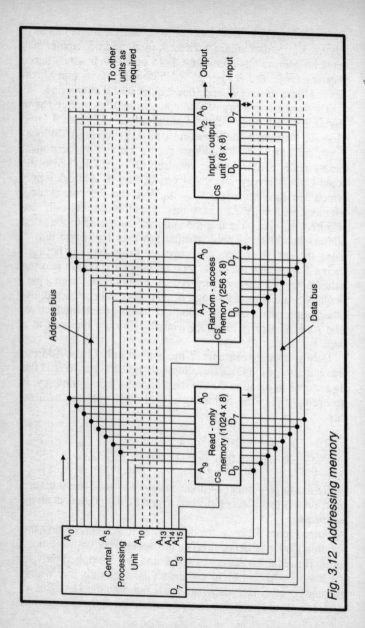

Fig. 3.12 Addressing memory

60

the sketch, the information is returned to the Central Processing Unit, i.e. the CPU has now read the data in location 200 in the Random-Access Memory.

From the Figure it can also be seen how the CPU addresses the Input-Output Unit with the subsequent flow of data.

3.4.2 Memory Organization

We now need to expand a little on the previous Section which shows how a memory element is located but it does not include the arrangements within. Figure 3.13(i) illustrates a 1-byte series of memory cells each capable of indicating a 0 or a 1. At (ii) in the figure is a "block" of memory of 5 separate addresses. As we have seen in the previous section, when the CPU addresses a particular byte, the digital information is read out onto the data bus. Such memory cells can be read electronical-

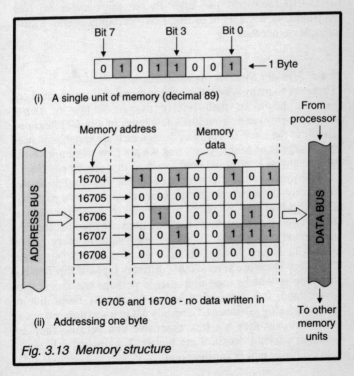

(i) A single unit of memory (decimal 89)

16705 and 16708 - no data written in

(ii) Addressing one byte

Fig. 3.13 Memory structure

ly as often as required and can also be reset, i.e. all cells at logic 0. As an example, suppose that the letter B is stored in memory location 16706. The processor gains access to this information by first placing the appropriate bits (0100000101000010 – the binary code for 16706) on the address bus whereupon this location only is unlocked and its contents (01000010 – the binary code for B) are placed on the data bus for transmission back to the processor. In the other direction the processor *writes* in the memory firstly by unlocking the location chosen and then placing the data bits on the data bus whereupon any data already existing in the memory location is first erased.

Note that although the information on the data bus is available to all memory locations, only the unlocked one can receive it. Also in this particular case the processor must know that 01000010 represents the letter B, not the number 66 (see Appendix 4), nor a set of instructions – certainly overall a most complex procedure.

3.4.3 Memory Systems (Semiconductor)

There are so many ways of arranging memory systems that here we can no more than briefly discuss a few of them. Requirements range from just a few bytes in a small integrated circuit to the more recent laser discs which are capable of storing hundreds of Megabytes – and we are now talking in terms of as many as a thousand books such as this one *on one disc*!

Many memory IC's store on the *bistable (flip-flop)* principle, especially those which are part of random-access memory. Each flip-flop employs either two bipolar transistors or alternatively two MOS transistors. For simplicity we consider the first mentioned and a basic circuit of one single memory cell is shown in Figure 3.14(i). This is known as an RS (*reset–set*) flip -flop. There are several other different types of flip-flop but this one is widely used and also is perhaps the simplest to understand. It is fast acting and is moderately insensitive to manufacturing tolerances. Generally MOS transistors are not so fast, however they are less expensive and because they are smaller, packing densities are higher. They are also likely to have a lower power consumption.

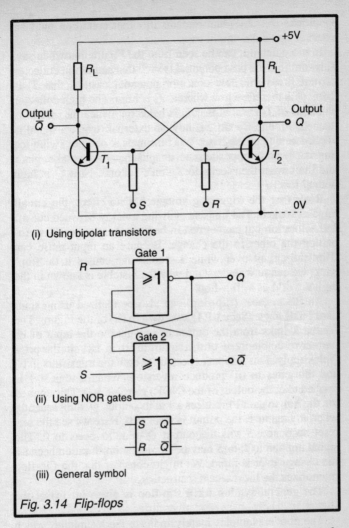

(i) Using bipolar transistors

Gate 1

R

$\geqslant 1$ ○ Q

Gate 2

$\geqslant 1$ ○ $\overline{Q}$

S

(ii) Using NOR gates

S	Q
R	$\overline{Q}$

(iii) General symbol

Fig. 3.14 Flip-flops

In the Figure there are two n-p-n transistors with their collector loads, R_L. Briefly one transistor is normally 'on' and this holds the other transistor 'off'. When an incoming signal turns the 'off' transistor to 'on', this automatically turns and holds the 'on' transistor 'off'. Accordingly the circuit has two stable conditions (bistable) and remains in either condition until an external signal changes it over.

In more detail it can be seen from the Figure that when say, T_1 is 'on' (i.e. the base potential is such that saturation collector current flows), its low collector potential ensures that T_2 is 'off'. $\overline{Q}$ is therefore low whereas Q is high. The high collector potential of T_2 ensures that T_1 is held 'on' hence the circuit is latched, T_1 'on', T_2 'off'. If now an external (trigger) signal is applied to one of the bases (via terminals R or S) to swing the transistor into its opposite state, a rapid change-over takes place and the circuit then locks to T_2 'on', T_1 'off'. Now $\overline{Q}$ is high with Q low.

Removing the triggering voltage has no effect, the circuit remains locked. The transistors swing quickly between cut-off and saturation but cannot rest in between because each is propelling the other in the change. Because an input pulse can 'flip' the circuit over while a second one causes it to 'flop' back, we can now understand why the bistable is known in the digital world as a 'flip-flop'.

An RS bistable (flip-flop) can also be realized using standard NOR gates (Sect.3.1.4) as shown in (ii) of the Figure. The feedback links from the output of one gate to the input of its partner resemble those of the circuit in (i), in fact similar principles apply. This is to be expected for both the transistors in (i) and the gates in (ii) produce inversion. When a logical 1 is applied to S, the output of the (NOR) gate 2 is at 0. This applied via the link to gate 1 produces a 1 at its output, Q. Subsequently when R goes to 1, the output is reset to 0. Here we see the set-reset sequence, S sets the output Q to 1, R resets to 0. The signal applied to R or S may be of very short duration because the change-over is rapid. We might consider that the flip-flop memorizes the most recent instruction.

The general symbol for a flip-flop is given in (iii) of the Figure.

The above examples merely indicate the techniques which may be employed when memory is required. There are many variations of memory cells and systems, e.g. the RS flip-flops mentioned above can be *gated* or *clocked*, meaning that a clock pulse has the ultimate control so that signals are only applied to the flip-flop with precise timing. There are many other types, generally serving somewhat different requirements or with added timing arrangements. More on the use of flip-flops, e.g. in shift registers, is contained in Section 3.5.1.

3.4.4 Memory Systems (Magnetic)

To understand magnetization we may need a little basic theory first, here simplified as much as possible. An electron spins on its own axis and carries an electric charge which has been labelled "negative". Moving charges give rise to magnetic fields hence each electron, because it is spinning, is equivalent to a tiny magnet. Nature in most cases arranges things so that the total magnetic effect of all the electrons in an atom is negligible through mutual cancellations. In some materials however this is not so and the whole atom behaves as a tiny magnet itself so exhibiting its own North and South poles. Materials well known for this effect are iron, steel, nickel and cobalt.

If an atom of a magnetic material is within a magnetic field, there will be a force pulling the North pole of the atom towards the South pole of the external field and vice versa. Given sufficient applied magnetic field strength, the atom aligns itself with the field. In a magnetically 'hard' metal such as steel, the atoms remain aligned even when the external magnetic field is removed. With all atom North poles pointing in one direction and South poles in the opposite, the steel itself exhibits residual magnetism, in effect it has become a permanent magnet. Accordingly if at any point on a thin magnetic material, a pulse of magnetisation arrives, a tiny spot of magnetism remains. This could easily be read later as a digital 1 and where no magnetism exists, a digital 0.

A coil of wire wound on a magnetic core will produce a magnetic flux when an electric current flows through it. If the coil is in close proximity to a magnetizable material, that material takes up a small amount of magnetism. This is how digital information is recorded (written). Equally if this 'spot' of magnetism moves over such a coil, an electromotive force is developed in the winding. This is how information is read. Here then we have a read/write head as used in both magnetic disc and tape systems.

MAGNETIC TAPE – for this a recording of digital signals is made on a moving magnetic medium, the tape. The tape itself is almost invariably a pliable yet strong plastic with a coating on one side of a magnetic material, usually consisting of fine particles of a magnetic oxide mixed with a binder which coats the particles to prevent bunching when a magnetic field is present. Digital information is recorded on or retrieved from the tape by a magnetic read/write head as illustrated in Figure 3.15. When a signal is present in the head windings a small area of the coating is magnetized, the direction of the remanent flux depending on whether a 0 or a 1 is stored. On playback the information stored is retrieved via the same read/write head when the flux cut by the head induces a voltage in the windings. Alternatively, for relatively slow speed systems, short bursts of low and high pure tones may be recorded.

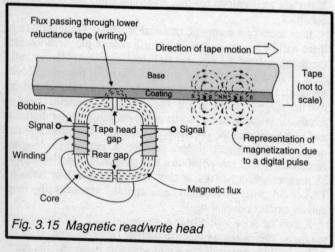

Fig. 3.15 Magnetic read/write head

Because tapes must be wound to the section required, the system is comparatively slow. It is known as *sequential access* and the lack of speed is clearly because mechanical rather than electronic means are required to provide access. Nevertheless it is a low-cost method which is capable of storing large quantities of information and it does not require movement of the read/write head as with the disc systems which follow.

FLOPPY DISCS – these are reasonably low-cost devices for random-access back-up storage. Discs are generally available of diameters 3.5 and 5.25 inches, mainly used in micro-computers and word processors. The magnetic medium is a circular, flexible material coated with a magnetic oxide compound. The disc is contained within a square rigid plastic case which has a central bush with which the drive spindle engages to rotate the disc. There is an aperture through which the disc is disclosed when it is inserted into the drive, the *head slot* (see Figure 3.16). When not in the drive, the head slot is concealed by a metal shutter to prevent fingers etc. ruining the disc. The read/write head operates in actual contact with the disc through the head slot aperture.

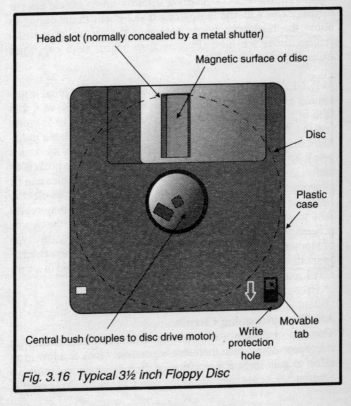

Head slot (normally concealed by a metal shutter)

Magnetic surface of disc

Disc

Plastic case

Central bush (couples to disc drive motor)

Write protection hole

Movable tab

Fig. 3.16 Typical 3½ inch Floppy Disc

Data on the disc is arranged in concentric circles known as *tracks*, with say, at least 40 tracks per disc. Discs may also be double-sided in which case two read/write heads are required. The heads are movable and can be made to jump quickly to any location (i.e. radius) on the disc. Data can be accessed reasonably quickly considering that this is a magnetic medium, i.e. generally in less than 100 ms. Capacity of, for example a double-sided 3.5 inch disc, can be as much as 1–2 M bytes (i.e. sufficient for some 150,000 – 300,000 words).

HARD or CARTRIDGE DISCS – these can hold much more information compared with a floppy disc. The magnetic medium is again magnetic oxide, this is coated on, for example an aluminium rigid disc, contained within a strong plastic case or cartridge. As with the floppy disc a slot opens in the casing to allow the read/write heads access to the recording surface. Access times are normally less than 75 ms with capacities exceeding 40 M bytes.

MAGNETIC-BUBBLE – here we consider storing digital information on minute magnetized *domains* (the bubbles) in a thin film of magnetic garnet. A domain is a tiny region of magnetism in a ferromagnetic material and garnet is an insoluble glass-like compound (the deep red transparent variety is used as a gem). To clear or erase the store, the bubbles can be broken up and made to disappear. To insert new data, new bubbles can be generated. Bubbles can be read by moving them by an electric field and then counting. The presence of a bubble may represent a digital 1, no bubble, a digital 0. Clearly the whole process is more than a little complex yet surprisingly this type of memory is very reliable. In addition because of the extremely small size of a bubble, millions of bits can be stored in a very small space.

3.5 Microprocessing Circuits

There is of course a multiplicity of circuits associated with microprocessing, here therefore we can only look at a few in an effort to gain some appreciation of their make-up and purpose. Section 3.4.3 considers flip-flops which are extensively used in

microprocessing systems, there are also many other types, a
few of which are discussed briefly below.

3.5.1 Shift Registers

A flip-flop we recall is a circuit which can store one bit of
memory. Accordingly to store a word of 8 bits, a line of 8 flip-
flops is required. We consider the type in which the data is fed
in serially one bit at a time and the stored data is moved sequen-
tially along the chain of flip-flops, collectively known as a *shift
register*. Although in practice shift registers are capable of storing many bits, even up to thousands, we are restricted here to
considering a simple 4-bit system.

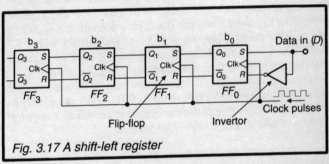

Fig. 3.17 A shift-left register

A shift register is therefore not unlike a memory location but
with the added facility that the stored bits can be shifted to left
or right according to the type of register. A typical circuit is
given in Figure 3.17, it is one of many but is chosen to demonstrate as simply as possible how such a register works. Note the
input of *clock pulses*. These are supplied from a system master
clock, the pulses shown arriving at some frequency probably
well above 1 MHz. Figure 3.14(iii) shows the general symbol
for a flip-flop and Figure 3.17 gives the basic circuit of one particular type of register. In this application there is no requirement for two inputs hence the addition of an invertor (a NOT
gate, Sect.3.1.3) which is added in series with the R input of the
FF_0 flip-flop. Considering this particular flip-flop:

when $D = 0$, therefore $S = 0$ and via the invertor, $R = 1$, therefore $Q_0 = 0$, $\overline{Q_0} = 1$.

When $D = 1$, therefore $S = 1$ and via the invertor, $R = 0$,

therefore $Q_0 = 1$, $\overline{Q_0} = 0$,

so, taking the output from Q_0, a high input on D sets the flip-flop to $Q_0 = 1$, a low input resets it.

Suppose that in Figure 3.17 the Q terminals all indicate reset, i.e. 0000 ($b_0 - b_3$) and next that D goes to 1. The next clock pulse arrives and FF_0 sets to $Q_0 = 1$ so that the register reads 0001. Now D goes to 0. Because $Q_0 = 1$ and $\overline{Q_0} = 0$ with S and R taking up these levels, FF_1 is prepared for action on the next clock pulse and FF_0 resets. When the next clock pulse arrives the bits stored become 0010, now preparing FF_2. When this toggles the number stored is 0100 and finally with FF_3, 1000. The 1 has shifted one place to the left with the vacated flip-flop resetting to 0 on the incidence of each clock pulse.

If on the other hand, D remains at logic 1 throughout, the stored bits change from 0000 to 0001, 0011, 0111 and finally to 1111. Accordingly this particular circuit is known as a *shift-left* register. There is also a *shift-right* version.

3.5.2 The Arithmetic and Logic Unit

This particular unit is an important part of any computer and in fact its name indicates what it does, i.e. all arithmetic functions (add, subtract, multiply and divide) with various logic functions (e.g. AND, OR, XOR – see Sect.3.1). It may also include inversion, shifting (Sect.3.5.1), incrementing and decrementing – all according to the requirements of the particular computing system.

We have examined the underlying principles involved in binary arithmetic in Sections 2.3.1 – 2.3.5 and here as a more practical example we consider a binary adder which simply performs the mathematical addition of binary digits. This is the basic arithmetical process because, as can be seen from the earlier considerations, binary subtraction can be considered as negative addition, multiplication as repeated addition and division as repeated negative addition. This may begin to sound complicated but it shows that all four common arithmetical processes can be based on binary addition and we will see that this itself depends on well known logic gates – not nearly as complicated as at first thought.

Half-Adders – when we ourselves add two numbers, each of one digit only, often we end up with an answer extending over two digits, e.g. 7, a single digit added to 5, another single digit results in 12, now of two digits. This might be expressed on paper as follows:

Column 2	Column 1	
	7	
	5	
1	2	(answer)

there has been a *carry-out* (C_o) of 1 from Column 1 to Column 2. The same happens with binary, there are four possible combinations of input signals resulting in sum and carry results as follows:

Digits to be added		Sum	Carry
A	B	S	C_o
0	0	0	0
0	1	1	0
1	0	1	0
1	1	0	1

A half-adder (*half* because there is more to come) has two inputs and two outputs. It must therefore add two binary digits and pass on the result together with the overflow or carry, C_o.

From the above table we see that $S = 1$ only when A and B differ – this can be provided by an exclusive-OR gate (Sect.3.1.5). Also $C_o = 1$ only when both A and B are 1 – this can be provided by an AND gate (Sect.3.1.1). Putting these two gates together therefore provides the half-adder facility as shown in Figure 3.18(i).

The half-adder therefore provides only half the operations necessary to do the complete job, remembering that there is no

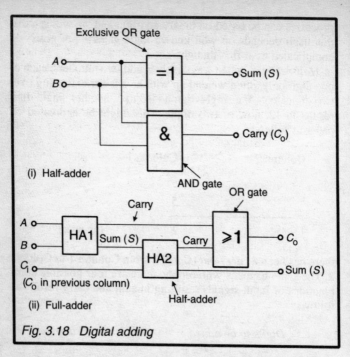

Fig. 3.18 Digital adding

provision for a carry-in, C_i. Two half-adders together however can do the complete job and as such are known as a *full-adder*. A truth-table for a full-adder is therefore as below. Note that it is assumed that there is a carry-in from the next lower-order position in the complete adder.

Digits to be added			Sum	Carry
A	B	C_i	S	C_o
0	0	0	0	0
0	0	1	1	0
0	1	0	1	0
0	1	1	0	1
1	0	0	1	0
1	0	1	0	1
1	1	0	0	1
1	1	1	1	1

72

A circuit to provide this facility is given in Figure 3.18(ii). We follow the system through for say, $A = 1$, $B = 0$, $C_i = 1$ (3rd line up in the table). HA1 has therefore an input $A = 1$, $B = 0$, hence with an output $S = 1$, $C_o = 0$. $S = 1$ is applied to HA2 together with C_o from the previous adder, now marked as C_i (to HA2). The output of HA2 is therefore $S = 0$, $C_o = 1$. The two carries (from HA1 and HA2) are applied to the OR-gate (Sect.3.1.2) with the resulting output of 1, hence the final result is $S = 0$, $C_o = 1$ as shown in the table.

The full-adder is the basic arithmetic unit, any number of these can be built up as required for adding large binary numbers, either in serial or parallel form.

3.5.3 Clocks and Counters

So far we have gained some appreciation of registers and arithmetical processing. In a computing system there is more, much more. There is a multitude of different units, all working digitally, which make up the complete system. Here we conclude our foray into microprocessing circuits with a look at clocks and counters, both are essential components in any computing system.

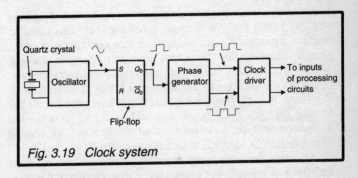

Fig. 3.19   Clock system

A *master clock* is the main timing device needed to control the timing of events throughout the whole system, it usually runs at a few megahertz. The frequency is almost invariably controlled by a quartz crystal as shown in Figure 3.19. A square-wave clock pulse must be generated and as an example this may be accomplished by the use of a sine wave oscillator

73

controlled by the crystal with its output connected to a flip-flop. From Section 3.4.3 we are reminded that when $S = 0$ then $Q = 0$, conversely when $S = 1$, $Q = 1$ and that the circuit toggles very rapidly. Accordingly the sine wave input results in a continuous setting and resetting of the flip-flop, so generating an almost perfect square wave. This is applied to a phase generator as shown, such a generator produces a number of phased outputs (two only are shown in the figure). Finally the clock driver amplifies each phase in order to provide sufficient power to operate the various clocked circuits. A reminder here, this is a single example of a clock system, inevitably there are many variations.

Counters: many digital processing systems need counters. Within a microprocessing system a counter usually has the capability of increasing a stored binary number by 1 each time it operates. Counters are generally divided into two types: (i) *synchronous* which uses clock pulses (see above) to control the time at which changes take place; and (ii) *asynchronous* in which one change of state initiates the next. In essence an asynchronous counter consists of an assembly of flip-flops so connected that the output of any one acts as a toggle input of the next.

Asynchronous counters generally work at lower speeds compared with the synchronous types for if it is required to read out the counter state at any time then counting must temporarily cease so that the output is stable during the read-out period. On the other hand, with the synchronous design each operation is controlled by a clock signal acting in parallel on all flip-flops. It might therefore appear that because the circuit has to wait for each clock pulse, it would be slower than for the asynchronous type, however because all the flip-flops change over together, read-out is in fact much faster.

Although there are many counter systems around, we need only look at a simple one to gain some appreciation of the basic principles; this is an asynchronous type illustrated by Figure 3.20. Three flip-flops are shown connected so that the output of each toggles the next adjacent one. Let us start with all outputs $Q_0 - Q_2$ at 0. On the arrival of the first clock pulse into FF_1, this triggers, hence Q_0 is set to 1 whereas Q_1 and Q_2 remain at 0. The second pulse restores Q_0 to 0 and triggers Q_1, while Q_2

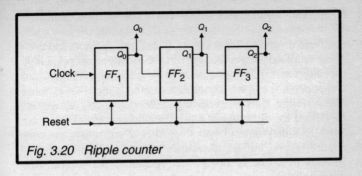

Fig. 3.20 Ripple counter

remains at 0. The sequence continues as shown below:

Pulse	Q_2	Q_1	Q_0
0	0	0	0
1	0	0	1
2	0	1	0
3	0	1	1
4	1	0	0
5	1	0	1
6	1	1	0
7	1	1	1
8	0	0	0

and we see that after 7 input pulses all the Q outputs are at 1.
Pulse 8 arrives and resets Q_0 to 0, hence Q_1 and Q_2 reset to 0 as
shown. Note from the table that the settings of the Q terminals
give the binary equivalents of the decimal count number.
Because the change in the output of each flip-flop initiates a
change in the next one, the system is also known as a *ripple
counter.*

The counting range for 4 flip-flops is therefore 0 – 15, for an
8-bit counter, up to 255 and for a 16-bit counter to 65,535.

3.6 Circuit Integration
Just another of the fascinating developments of modern times.
Gone are the days of circuit boards laden with heavy

components and almost lost in a web of coloured wires. Instead we now have the *integrated circuit* (IC), starting off as a small component yet containing several transistors, resistors and even some small capacitors (but only in the picofarad range). Large capacitors and inductors cannot be included, accordingly such components are either connected externally or what is more likely, design aims at excluding such components altogether. Re-design for this purpose has been most successful. Now the latest IC's may be no larger than some 2 cm square yet containing several million transistors with the capability of performing over one or two billion operations per *second*. The mind boggles!

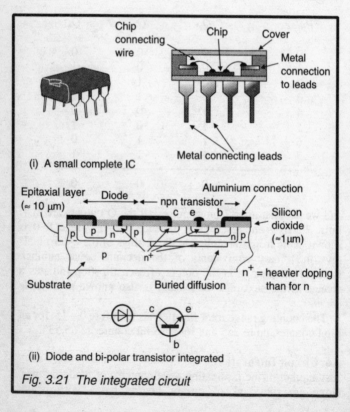

(i) A small complete IC

(ii) Diode and bi-polar transistor integrated

Fig. 3.21 The integrated circuit

Back to earth, we consider a small IC, packaged as shown in Figure 3.21(i). Within the block is the circuit itself, contained on the small *chip* as shown. Considering the electronic circuitry it contains, the chip is not just small, it is minute, perhaps no more than a few square millimetres in area, it is because of its dimunitive size that it has to be mounted within the protective case. Power consumption is generally small with working voltages usually of 5 but possibly higher.

The modern IC is described as *monolithic* (from Greek, "single block") because all components plus interconnections are contained on a single chip of silicon or gallium arsenide (the *substrate*). Gallium arsenide has a higher resistivity so provides greater isolation between components on it.

At (ii) in the figure is shown just one example of the technology. This shows the integration of two components only, a semiconductor diode connected to the collector of a bipolar transistor. The substrate has a flat surface into which the various impurities for the n- and p-type regions are diffused. Recalling that one micrometre is one-thousandth of one millimetre, the extremely small size of the components in the figure can be appreciated. Certainly the cross-section of an IC as shown looks more complicated than one might expect considering that only two components are involved. This is mainly because *isolation* techniques must be employed to ensure that the conductivity of the substrate does not allow components to be in electrical contact with each other.

Chapter 4

CONVERSION BETWEEN ANALOGUE AND DIGITAL STRUCTURES

We can understand the need by recalling that we ourselves are analogue yet nowadays many transmission systems work digitally. As an example a telephone handset works in analogue simply because it is inevitably connected to a user who has no choice but to be analogue. Soon after the analogue speech signals have left the premises however (or perhaps even *before*) there is a possibility that the signals will be converted into digital for transmission onwards. At the distant end conversion back to analogue must take place. There must therefore be devices which are capable of changing between the two systems, i.e. an *analogue-to-digital converter*, also a *digital-to-analogue converter*.

4.1 Digital-to-Analogue Conversion

Because this is a more straightforward procedure than conversion in the opposite direction, it is considered first. A 4-bit system is sufficient to demonstrate the principles. What we are aiming for first is a current which is proportional to the numerical content of a string of 4 bits, $b_3 - b_0$. If a current I_0 represents b_0, then $2I_0$ is needed to represent b_1, $4I_0$ for b_2, etc., since b_1 is twice and b_2 is four times the value of b_0. It is therefore simply a matter of reducing the value of the series resistance to one-half each time we move one digit towards the most significant (in this example, b_3). This is shown diagrammatically in Figure 4.1(i). Then:

$$I_0 = \frac{V}{16R} \qquad I_1 = \frac{V}{8R} = 2I_0, \qquad \text{also } I_2 = 4I_0 \text{ and } I_3 = 8I_0$$

giving, as required, currents each related to the significance of the bit represented. What is of equal importance is that the currents are additive, for example, if I_0 and I_3 only are effective, the total current through the ammeter is $(I_0 + I_3)$.

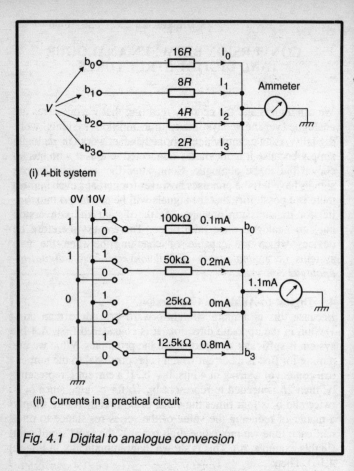

(i) 4-bit system

(ii) Currents in a practical circuit

Fig. 4.1 Digital to analogue conversion

Next we need to connect V when the incoming bit is a 1 but not when 0. Logic 1 cannot be connected directly because the technique relies on V being constant, therefore a separate regulated supply for V must be used, connected to an input terminal only when a 1 is present. For such switches, a practical arrangement might use bipolar transistors connected as emitter followers for low output resistance. In Figure 4.1(ii) the switches are shown diagrammatically and typical values are assigned to the resistors with the resultant currents for an input 1011. The output current has a value of 0.1 mA for each unit value of the input, for example:

0000 results in 0 mA current
0001 results in 0.1 mA current
0010 results in 0.2 mA current
0011 results in (0.2 + 0.1) = 0.3 mA current
1111 results in 1.5 mA current,

a linear relationship which can be plotted as a graph as in Figure 4.2. This is a *staircase* waveform, in this case hardly a smooth line. This is because we have only a 4-bit system at our disposal, it is capable of dividing the analogue range into no more than 16 separate output currents, i.e. the smallest change is 1/16 of full output. Given, say a 10-bit system, each step is reduced to 1/1024 of full output, a much improved *resolution* with the staircase tending more towards a straight line.

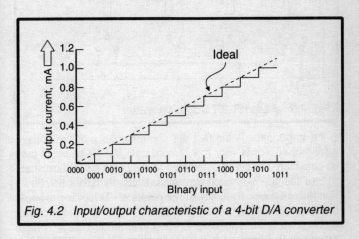

Fig. 4.2 *Input/output characteristic of a 4-bit D/A converter*

A converter of this type may be arranged for an analogue output voltage instead of current by use of an *operational amplifier.* The ammeter cannot simply be replaced by a resistor across which the voltage is taken because additional resistance in the chain upsets the linearity. An operational amplifier does the job without this complication.

4.1.1 R – 2R Conversion

The simple 4-digit system described above has several failings, perhaps the most important is that it requires accurate resistances over a wide range of values, e.g. for a 32-bit system, 32 resistances are required, all of different values. However a system known as the R – 2R Ladder avoids this difficulty by use of two values of resistance only (R and 2R). The basic circuit of a 4-digit converter is shown in Figure 4.3. Each incoming bit of the digital word to be converted operates an electronic switch which connects a 2R resistance to the common line if the value of the bit is 0, but to the reference voltage if it is a 1.

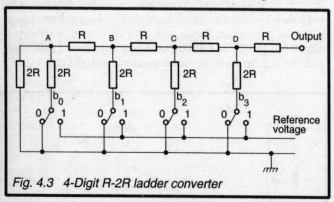

Fig. 4.3   4-Digit R-2R ladder converter

Of importance is the fact that the impedance of the voltage reference source is very low, accordingly the 2R resistors may be considered as being connected to the common line irrespective of the $b_0 - b_3$ switch positions. It can therefore be shown that the resistance from any of the points A – D looking towards the closed end of the ladder is always 2R. Using various circuit theorems it is then possible to show that the reference voltage gives rise to an output current proportional to $(I_1 + I_2/2 + I_3/4 + I_4/8)$ and here we see again how incoming binary digits can have their individual (logic 1) values summed up according to their significance.

It must be emphasized that this is only one of the several different methods of digital-to-analogue conversion and of course all this complex technology is easily contained within a single integrated circuit.

4.2 Sampling

Fundamental to the technique of changing in the opposite direction, i.e. from analogue to digital, is the process of *sampling*.

This is a technique in which only certain levels of a signal are measured in order to produce the digital equivalent which is representative of the information contained within the original signal. Accordingly samples or measurements of the voltage of the analogue wave are taken at certain (usually regular) time intervals. To obtain a single value for the sample it should be measured over a very short period of time so that amplitude changes during the sampling time are insignificant.

Sampling generates a train of amplitude modulated pulses and clearly the greater the sampling frequency, the more information about the original signal is transmitted. However it has been shown that if a complex analogue signal is sampled at regular intervals of time and at a rate higher than twice the highest signal frequency, then the samples contain all the information of the original signal. This feature has contributed greatly towards the success of digital transmission. As an example, telephony signals in which the highest analogue frequency is 3.4 kHz are usually sampled at 8 kHz and a colour television signal of just over 5 MHz needs to be sampled at at least 11 MHz.

If we now consider a practical digital system working to say, 8 bits, Appendix 3 shows that 256 different codes will be available. Effectively this means that the amplitude range of the analogue signal cannot be sampled precisely but only to the nearest of the 256 levels, rather like rounding numbers or money up or down. This is in fact working in steps and representing a signal by steps or discrete levels in this way is called *quantizing*. We cannot show 256 levels on a diagram, so let us settle for a 4-digit system as shown in Figure 4.4.

A 4-digit system allows $2^4 = 16$ different levels of the analogue waveform to be examined. The Figure shows the 16 sampling levels (in digital systems the levels are invariably numbered starting from 0) and for example, a small portion of a waveform which is being sampled 4 times at, say 125 μs intervals (i.e. at 8 kHz). At the point which is marked $t = 0$ μs the timing of this first sample coincides exactly with the signal

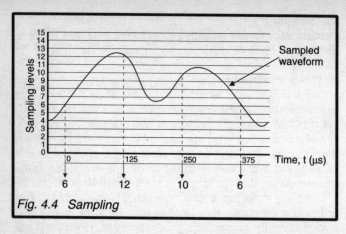

Fig. 4.4 Sampling

being at level 6. 125 μs later we find that the position of the second sample is not so clearly defined, it is between sampling levels 12 and 13. The equipment can automatically round up, round down or take the nearest. In the figure we show that it has been rounded down to sampling level 12. The third sample has been taken when the waveform is at level 10 and the last has been rounded down to level 6. These values are then held temporarily and are transmitted to equipment which changes them into the appropriate digital form, one method of doing so is considered next.

4.3 Analogue-to-Digital Conversion

Very briefly, the *Successive Approximation* system compares each analogue voltage (e.g. from Fig.4.4) with internally generated ones from digital values which at each comparison move one step nearer the final answer. This is generally explained by use of a *flow diagram* but it would be unwise of us to plod rather painfully through one of these, so here is a brief resumé of the operation.

The working range of the converter is divided into two and a *comparator* decides whether the analogue input is above or below the mid-point. The range has now been reduced to one half. The selected half is divided into two again and the input is compared with the mid-point to decide in which half it lies. These two operations have now located which quarter of the full range contains the input analogue value. The process is repeated to determine which eighth, sixteenth, etc., section of the range contains the input value. This finally produces one bit of the binary output. The whole process is then repeated for each bit.

Clearly the greater the number of bits used by a converter, the higher the accuracy, hence practical converters may be based on up to 32 bits or more. This is just one of the many different systems in use. Finally we must appreciate that whereas from the descriptions above it might be considered that conversion between the two structures is tedious and time-consuming, processors work at a very high rate of thousands or even millions of operations per second. Thus to use a colloquial expression, "the job is done in less than no time".

Chapter 5

TRANSMISSION SYSTEMS

Literally we can take the word "transmission" as meaning "serving to communicate" so both analogue and digital systems are classed under this heading. We have touched on the idea of information flow in Chapter 1, here we look more closely at the practical aspects of the transmission of information, but mainly digital.

In the early days of telephony bandwidth was a problem, there just was not enough to go round. Moreover wherever there are wires in close proximity, capacitance is there to attenuate the higher frequencies. From those early days to the present many new and greatly improved transmission systems have been developed, mainly to provide greater bandwidths to satisfy the growing need for local and world-wide communication. These included carrier systems over coaxial and submarine cables, microwave and satellite transmission and more recently, optical fibre systems. The optical fibre has really come to our rescue for it can now be operated at bandwidths unthinkable not so many years ago, and at reasonably low cost. Development continues apace.

An important factor in the reasons for converting information into a digital form is the advantage of regenerative digital transmission (see Chapter 1). Briefly, a regenerative repeater decides what an incoming digital train was like when it was first generated and then transmits onwards pulses identical with that original. Signal imperfections are therefore eliminated at each repeater and do not build up as the signal travels along the circuit as is the case with analogue. There are many facets to digital transmission and here we first consider one extensively in use and therefore an important one. This is the *pulse code modulation* system (p.c.m.), used extensively with optical fibre and with radio and satellite transmission systems.

5.1 Pulse Code Modulation

Before pulse code modulation came along, the only technique for combining several individual channels (i.e. each carrying a separate telephone conversation) was known as *frequency division multiplex*. This is a completely analogue system in which each channel occupies a different frequency band. We will see next that p.c.m. differs fundamentally in that each channel occupies a different *time slot* and no two channels are effective at the same time.

When we first make the acquaintance with p.c.m., things may seem more than a little complicated. In fact they are, so we first look at the basic idea of the system, then again in a more practical way but never in great detail otherwise complications may get out of hand. (For the benefit of readers who do not wish to plod through the technicalities of the system, there is a resumé in Sect.5.1.6.)

A p.c.m. system may be considered to be the combination of several processes:

(1) assuming the originating signal to be analogue (most are), it is first s*ampled*, i.e. measured regularly. The samples are in the form of short duration pulses (Sect.1.4) of height according to the voltage of the waveform at the time of sampling;

(2) the *pulse amplitude modulation* pulses (Sect.5.2.1) so generated are changed to pulse code modulation by a *coder* which measures the height of each pulse and converts this height into the corresponding binary digital code, i.e. a series of pulses of constant height;

(3) many channels are combined on a time basis, each channel of a multi-channel system being sampled in its turn. The stream of pulses is transmitted to the distant end;

(4) digital pulses transmitted by line may suffer distortion so are regenerated (Sect.1.4.2) before there is a possibility of being unable to distinguish between a 0 and a 1;

(5) at the distant end each channel undergoes *decoding* in which the incoming binary digital streams are directed to a digital-to-analogue converter to produce a replica of the original sending-end p.a.m. pulses. Full demodulation is accomplished simply by the use of a low-pass filter, the output of which is a copy of the original input analogue waveform.

Here we consider a 32-channel pulse code modulation system as used extensively in telephone systems. The method is based on *time-division multiplexing*, i.e. a number of separate channels is operated over a single transmission circuit on a time basis. In such a system the whole transmission circuit is allocated to each channel in turn but only for a fraction of the time. Thus the line to the distant end is available to Channel 1 for only a given period of time, then to Channel 2, followed by Channel 3, etc. Multiplexing is considered in more detail in Section 5.3.

When the last channel has been served, the allocation repeats. Exposing all channels to the line once constitutes a *frame* which contains time slots, one per channel. It is perhaps easier to appreciate what happens by assigning times to the events so, assuming commercial speech channels and a sampling rate of 8 kHz (Sect.4.2), a sampling method might be imagined as in Figure 5.1(i) for a 32-channel arrangement. Switch S rotates 8,000 times in one second, i.e. 125 μs per revolution, hence connecting each channel for a little less than $125/32 = 3.91$ μs. The analogue signal has arrived via a low-pass filter. During each 3.91 μs sampling time the analogue signal voltage on the input is measured (see also Fig.4.4) and passed to the *encoder*. For one revolution of switch S, the encoder receives the information for one frame. The encoder changes from analogue to digital (see below) so assuming Channel 1 to have at the instant of sampling a signal voltage of 35 mV, this applied to the encoder results in an output pulse train 00100011 (Appendix 4). At this instant Channel 1 is said to be occupying its time slot. For more practice, let us imagine that the Channel 2 signal has a value of 69 mV (01000101), Channel 3, 250 mV (11111010) and Channel 32, 41 mV (00101001). The signal output from the encoder would then be as shown in Figure 5.1(ii).

Frame 2 is shown commencing with Channel 1 at its next sampled value at 125 μs after the first at say, 29 mV (00011101). These line signals are regenerated along the route as necessary and finally again at the receiving end.

Sampling is considered in greater detail in Chapter 4 and for p.c.m. the general principles are the same.

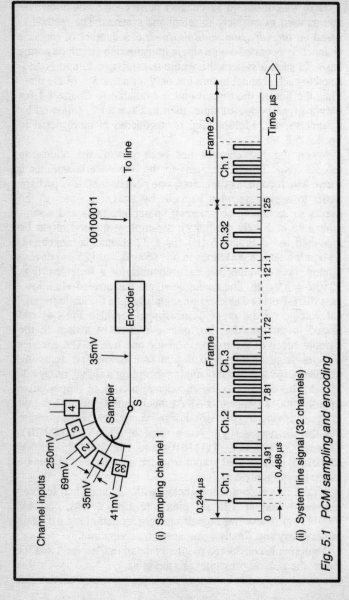

Fig. 5.1 PCM sampling and encoding

(i) Sampling channel 1

(ii) System line signal (32 channels)

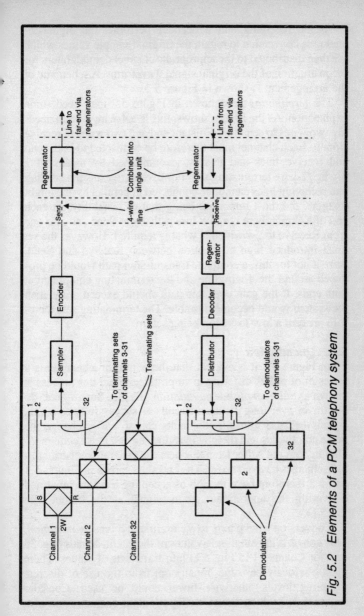

Fig. 5.2 Elements of a PCM telephony system

At the receiving end a decoder performs the digital-to-analogue conversion to regain the original sample values which are then distributed to the appropriate channel demodulators for reconstruction of the original signal waveforms. A schematic of the arrangement is shown in Figure 5.2.

The *terminating sets* shown in Figure 5.2 may need some explanation. As the Figure shows, this is a 4-wire system needing two wires to send to the distant end and two wires to receive from it. Each channel must therefore be connected to both send and receive lines and this is accomplished by means of a 4-wire /2-wire terminating set. For several reasons the sending and receiving lines cannot be connected in parallel as one might imagine, the most important being that of instability. At each end of a circuit there is a low-loss path 2w to Send and also one from Receive to 2w which is what is required. However the set must introduce high attenuation between Receive and Send, were it not for this, a complete transmission path would be produced around the 4-wire line and the terminating equipment at both ends. If the gain over this path should exceed unity, then the system would become unstable. The terminating sets therefore prevent a low-loss loop being set up.

5.1.1 *Quantization*

From Figure 5.1 it is evident that the output of a sampler is a series of of pulses differing in amplitude, in fact this process is known as *pulse amplitude modulation* (p.a.m.). Such signals do not travel over long distance circuits as successfully as p.c.m. signals because transmission faults can so easily change the pulse amplitudes and thereby introduce errors. Pulse code modulation does not suffer from this because generally pulse amplitude changes have no effect. The encoders shown in Figures 5.1 and 5.2 therefore have the job of accepting a p.a.m. input and delivering the appropriate p.c.m. signal at the output (see Fig.5.1).

Conversion from p.a.m. to p.c.m. first involves *quantization*. This converts the amplitude values of the p.a.m. signals (e.g. 35 mV for Channel 1 in Fig. 5.1) into finite sets of values. There must obviously be some impairment from the use of discrete sampling levels otherwise fewer could be used. Consider Figure 5.3(i) which shows an input/output characteristic of a

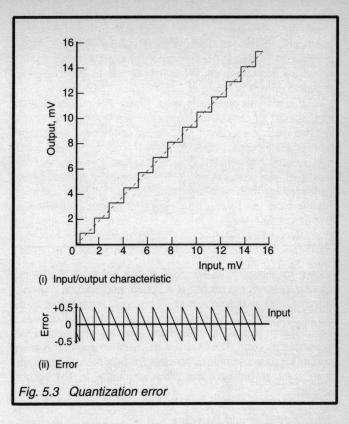

(i) Input/output characteristic

(ii) Error

Fig. 5.3 Quantization error

quantization system. The ideal characteristic is a straight line such that whatever the amplitude of the input, that becomes the pulse amplitude at the output. However the practical characteristic has a staircase form, for example for all inputs between just over 0.5 and 1.5, the output is consistently 1.0. We can look at the discrepancy between practical and ideal a little more closely as shown in the table on page 94. It is then possible to draw the graph of quantization error as in Figure 5.3(ii). Effectively therefore the sampler output can be considered as a series of p.a.m. pulses which when reconstructed are equivalent to ideal pulses disfigured by the addition of an error signal. The graph shows the latter to be of triangular form and this can be

Input	Output	Error
0	0	0
0.25	0	−0.25
0.5	0	−0.5
0.51	1.0	+0.49
0.75	1.0	+0.25
1.0	1.0	0
1.25	1.0	−0.25
1.5	1.0	−0.5
1.51	2.0	+0.49
1.75	2.0	+0.25
⋮	⋮	⋮
⋮	⋮	⋮

shown to abound with harmonics. The result of this is that quantization error gives rise to a system noise which is usually referred to as *quantization noise*. This noise is generated by the p.c.m. system itself, there is always the problem of unwanted noise being picked up elsewhere, here is a system which generates its own! Thus we see the need to employ as many coding digits per sample as possible for then the steps in Figure 5.3(i) and accordingly the error amplitude in (ii) become smaller.

5.1.2 Encoding and Decoding
The requirement of an encoder and of a decoder in a p.c.m. system is illustrated in Figure 5.2.

Encoder – the encoder quantizes and then codes the incoming p.a.m. signals in order to change to the p.c.m. form. For encoding there are several designs, even an early one based on a cathode-ray tube. A more modern design consists of a series of *comparators* which we might describe as pulse height discriminators. An incoming p.a.m. pulse is held constant while its amplitude is compared with a number of equally spaced reference levels. This is achieved by the bank of comparators as illustrated in Figure 5.4. Each comparator has an output only if the input level lies between its two reference voltages. These

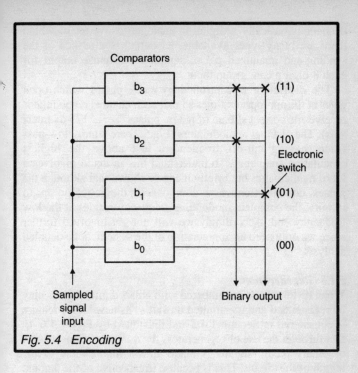

Comparators

b_3 (11)

b_2 (10)

Electronic switch

b_1 (01)

b_0 (00)

Sampled signal input

Binary output

Fig. 5.4   Encoding

are set to the two levels bounding the quantization interval. Accordingly the array of comparators determines to which level the signal amplitude is nearest. The particular comparator affected then produces a binary output by operating its associated electronic switch. Overall therefore the coder output provides the binary equivalent of the incoming p.a.m. signal. Figure 5.4 illustrates this by showing the arrangement for a hypothetical 4-digit system, e.g. for a high-level sampled signal input the digital output is 11, for the lowest level, 00.

Decoder – this performs the opposite function to that of an encoder by converting binary code words into equivalent pulses having amplitudes according to the corresponding quantization level. The stream of binary digits is first divided into 8-digit groups, correct grouping being maintained by reception of a synchronizing signal from the sending end. Decoding of each group then proceeds as soon as the eighth digit is received. The decoder is basically a digital-to-analogue converter of which there are many types available, its output is a replica of the sending-end quantized p.a.m. samples, one pulse output for each 8-digit p.c.m. group input.

The distributor is controlled by clock pulses which open gates at the appropriate times so that each channel demodulator receives its correct stream of p.a.m. pulses (i.e. at 125 µs intervals). The channel demodulators (Fig.5.2) are simply low-pass filters having cut-off frequencies just above the highest modulating frequency. To understand this in detail involves a lot of mathematics but briefly it can be shown that although the pulses contain frequency components theoretically up to infinity, the complete modulating frequency resides at the low frequency end. Accordingly we will not get involved further since we only need an appreciation of the system, not a detailed analysis.

5.1.3 Regeneration

When distorted and encumbered with noise, digital signals may be regenerated and transmitted onwards "as new". This feature is considered in Section 1.4.2 and illustrated by Figure 1.6. In fact through the use of regenerators the quality of transmission of binary p.c.m. signals is made almost independent of the length of the circuit. This is because irrespective of the amount of distortion a pulse suffers or how much noise is picked up on the way, then as long as the pulse can be recognized electronically as such at some distant point, a new clean one can be generated. Normal amplification as with analogue systems would amplify the pulse not only with all its distortions, but also with the noise. Regeneration can be employed as often as is required.

5.1.4 Error Checking

Of course none of the above is possible without some risk of error, however small. It is clear that errors in a digital system (i.e. 0's and 1's being mistaken for each other) have an importance depending on the type of information being carried. An error or two in a telephony p.c.m. system would probably pass unnoticed. On the other hand, errors in a computer system, especially when numbers are involved, are more serious because a single error changes the whole number. The complexity of an error detection system therefore depends on the application of the system.

In a simple system the encoder adds *redundant* symbols for checking purposes; at the other end of the channel the decoder, knowing the encoding system, is able to check constantly what is received. Naturally the error checking system reduces the rate of information flow because redundant symbols have to be used.

A digital system is assessed by its *bit error rate* which is defined as the number of bits received in error to the total transmitted. A good system may have a bit error rate not exceeding 1 in 10^6 for most of the time. Many complex systems require bit error rates considerably better than this.

Perhaps the simplest method of detecting errors is the one known as *parity checking* (Sect.2.1.1). Taking the simplest code which requires 7 bits in length to express a single character, there is one bit spare in the normal byte (8 bits). The first or the eighth position is conveniently used for a parity (equality) bit which is used simply to indicate whether all is well or not.

An *odd parity generator* adds a single logical 1 when doing so makes the total number of 1's in the byte odd. An *even parity generator* similarly arranges for an even number of 1's. As an example the decimal number 85 might be transmitted as:

odd parity   – 1 (parity) followed by 1010101   or

even parity   – 0 (parity) followed by 1010101.

The parity bit might equally follow the code. At the receiving end every byte is tested for the chosen parity. A positive result in the test is a good indication of successful transmission, but of course not a guarantee. The system has some weaknesses but in most situations these are greatly outweighed by the overall reduced likelihood of undetected error. Additional arrangements enable the distant end to request retransmission of a block of data in which an error is noted.

5.1.5 Bandwidth
This for p.c.m. transmission is not always easily calculated because we have to relate a transmission rate in bits per second

with the frequency band required in hertz. Considering the bit rate for our 32 channel system:

Number of bits per frame $= 8 \times 32 = 256$

there are 8,000 frames per second

therefore line bit rate $= 256 \times 8,000 = 2.048$ M bit/s

and as a rough guide we might use the same figure for bandwidth, i.e. 2 MHz. However most practical systems manage with much less because digital transmission is fairly tolerant of noise and circuit distortions, say, even down to half this amount, i.e. about 1 MHz. Much depends on the characteristics of the transmission path however.

5.1.6 A P.C.M. Abstract

The foregoing sections describing the essence of a p.c.m. system may be more than some readers are happy with on first reading. Accordingly, as mentioned in Section 5.1, we end the discourse with a summary of the major facets of a complete system. The various stages are illustrated by Figure 5.5:

(i)   shows a small part of an incoming analogue wave

at (ii)   a sample of magnitude v is taken at time t

(iii)   shows the coding process. The p.a.m. sample of magnitude v (say 13 mV) is translated into its p.c.m. equivalent 1101. Some quantization noise has been added. This p.c.m. signal is now to be transmitted to the distant end;

(iv)   a single p.c.m. pulse is shown having deteriorated in shape and gathered extraneous noise on its journey;

(v)   the pulse meets a regenerator and reappears as new. Regeneration is applied as often as is necessary;

(vi)   the p.c.m. signal (e.g. 1101) arrives at the distant end and is applied to the decoder. The output of the decoder is a single p.a.m. pulse similar to the original in (iii);

(vii)   this p.a.m. pulse passes through a low-pass filter. With other earlier and later pulses similarly reconstructed, a copy of the original wave as in (i) is generated.

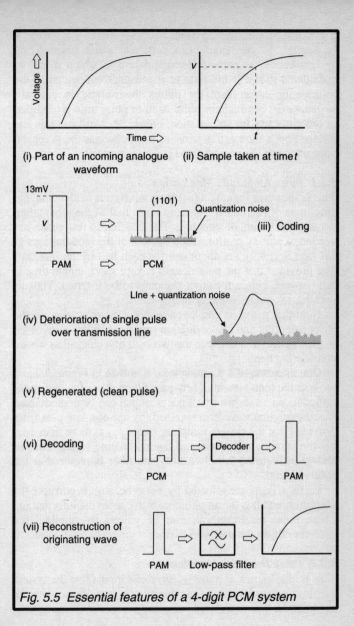

Fig. 5.5 Essential features of a 4-digit PCM system

5.2 Pulse Modulation Systems

In Section 5.1 we examine a particular pulse transmission system known as pulse *code* modulation in which it can be considered that it is the code at any instant which carries the information rather than the pulses themselves. In contrast, systems exist in which the pulse itself or pulse train is modified in order to carry the information. Figure 5.6 illustrates this and we see how a modulating wave as in (i) changes the graphical appearance of the unmodulated pulse train in (ii).

5.2.1 Pulse Amplitude Modulation

This is shown in Figure 5.6(iii) from which it is evident that the amplitude of each pulse is according to that of the modulating wave at the instant of sampling. The fact that so few pulses are needed to sense the information content of the modulating signal (see Sect.4.2), i.e. about one for each half cycle, indicates that provided that the pulse length is kept short, ample time is left between pulses for other channels to be inserted. Thus as with p.c.m., p.a.m. is easily multiplexed.

Note that p.a.m. is employed *within* a p.c.m. system in the wave sampling and reconstruction processes, it is not involved in the transmission between the two ends of a channel as we are considering here.

One direction of a p.a.m. system is shown in Figure 5.7 and we note the requirement of low-pass filters. As previously mentioned it can be shown that a p.a.m. signal can be demodulated (i.e. the original waveform regained) by use of a low-pass filter provided that the system sampling frequency is more than double the maximum frequency of the modulating signal. Thus as shown in Figure 5.7, only a low-pass filter is required at the receiving end.

P.a.m. signals are affected by noise because it corrupts the amplitude and it is the amplitude which carries the information. Some noise reduction can also be gained by 'muting' the receiver during the pulse-off periods.

5.2.2 Pulse Duration Modulation

This is also known as *pulse width modulation*. Here the system employs pulses having a time duration in accordance with the modulation. The modulated pulse commences at the same time

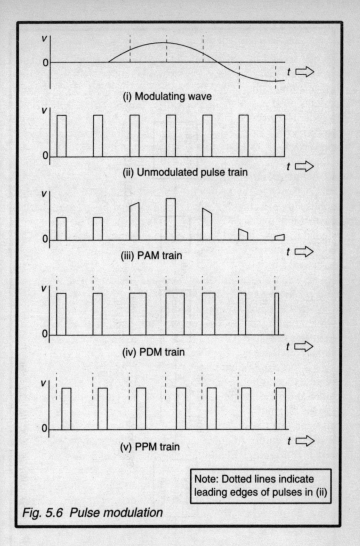

Note: Dotted lines indicate leading edges of pulses in (ii)

Fig. 5.6 Pulse modulation

as its unmodulated counterpart but its trailing edge is retarded in time for positive excursions of the modulating wave and advanced in time for the negative excursions. Figure 5.6 shows at (iv) how the duration (or width) therefore varies.

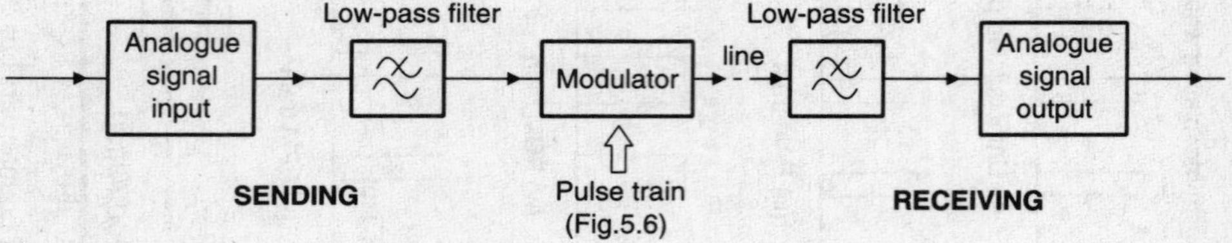

Fig. 5.7 Pulse Amplitude Modulation system

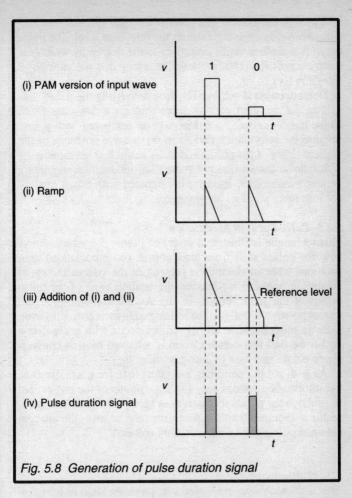

(i) PAM version of input wave

(ii) Ramp

(iii) Addition of (i) and (ii) — Reference level

(iv) Pulse duration signal

Fig. 5.8 Generation of pulse duration signal

One method of generating a p.d.m. signal is via a periodic *ramp* impressed on the p.a.m. version of the input wave. A ramp may be described as a pulse with a sloping edge as shown in Figure 5.8 at (ii). The ramp frequency is synchronized with that of the pulse amplitude modulation shown at (i). At (iii) is shown the effect of combining (i) and (ii). This waveform is next applied to a comparator which has a reference level as indicated in the sketch. The comparator only produces an output pulse while the input exceeds the reference level. The pulse duration therefore varies according to the degree by which the ramp exceeds the reference level, resulting in a p.d.m. train as shown in (iv).

Demodulation is achieved by first converting the p.d.m. signals to p.a.m., then passing them through a low-pass filter. Noise has less effect on p.d.m. signals compared with p.a.m. because the information resides in the relative positions of the vertical edges of the pulses and these suffer less corruption.

It can be shown that pulse duration modulation requires a greater transmission bandwidth compared with p.a.m. mainly because narrow pulses are involved.

5.2.3 Pulse Position Modulation

This technique is illustrated in (v) of Figure 5.6 which shows how the pulses shift from their normal (no modulation) time positions when modulation is present. In the system shown, at maximum negative modulation the leading edge of the pulse occurs at the same time as in (ii). As the modulating signal moves positively, delay in the leading edge increases, thus even with no modulation at all, the pulses occur with some delay. Again we find that demodulation is achieved by first converting to p.a.m. and then by low-pass filtering.

As with p.d.m., noise has less effect than for p.a.m. because the information resides only in the positions of the pulses, not so much in the pulses themselves. A greater transmission bandwidth is required than for p.a.m. mainly because the spacing between pulses can be considerably reduced.

5.3 Multiplexing

This is the technique employed when a single short or long distance connection needs to be shared by several signals which are completely independent of each other, a system we have seen in outline in Section 5.1 for p.c.m. *Time Division Multiplexing* is especially suited to pulse transmission systems and it operates basically by dividing a period of time into equal "slots", each signal being allocated a slot for its own exclusive use in turn.

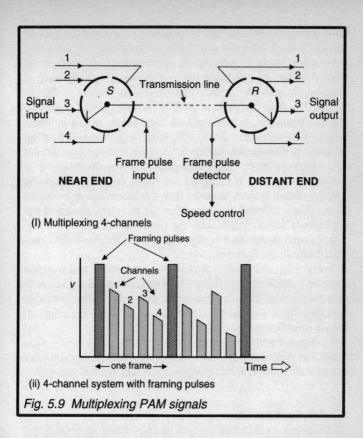

(I) Multiplexing 4-channels

(ii) 4-channel system with framing pulses

Fig. 5.9 Multiplexing PAM signals

From Section 5.2 it is evident that of the three pulse systems discussed, only p.a.m. pulses rise and fall at regular intervals because it is the pulse height only which matters. With pulse duration and pulse position systems, multiplexing clearly requires certain restraints otherwise pulses for one channel may overlap those of an adjacent channel and hence give rise to interference.

Consider the elementary 4-channel system illustrated by Figure 5.9(i). Here we have signals arriving from four separate inputs, each of which has to be allocated a through connection to the distant end in turn. This involves the switch S as shown. All very straightforward but now the difficulty arises of transmitting pulses from one input channel to the correct distant end output channel. There is also the need to ensure that the S and R switches rotate at exactly the same speed. This is accomplished by use of a *framing pulse* at the sending end which is interleaved with the transmitted pulses as shown in Figure 5.9(ii). The framing pulse is used for timing only, it carries no other information, accordingly all such pulses are of constant height. It is now clear that synchronization of the two rotating switches is paramount. This is achieved at the commencement of a transmission by slight changes to the rotational speed of switch R until the framing pulses "lock in" whereupon the speed control system ensures that synchronization is maintained. Each channel at the near end is therefore linked to the appropriate ongoing channel at the distant end. Needless to say, rotary switches are not employed as shown, the inevitable integrated circuit surely takes over.

For p.d.m. and p.p.m., maximum pulse width and position must be controlled so that gaps between pulses are sufficient to prevent overlap. Framing pulses are easily detectable provided that they have a different height compared with the constant height information pulses.

Compared with frequency division multiplex, time division multiplex systems are less complicated and less expensive because accurate and therefore costly filters are not required.

5.4 Information Theory

The concept of information flow is introduced in Section 1.1 and it is clear that communication and information flow are almost inseparable. Here we probe a little further but certainly not in great depth, our main aim being to understand the importance of the signal-to-noise ratio of a transmission channel although not forgetting the benefits digital transmission now gives us through the principle of regeneration (Sect.5.1.3).

The formulae introduced here take into account the various features of a transmission channel which affect the rate of information flow, i.e. they enable *channel capacity* to be calculated. The more information we try to squeeze through a channel, the greater the likelihood of error, especially when noise is present. We ought therefore to define *noise* first. Noise in communication systems results from the advent of spurious signals, either injected from outside or generated within the channel itself. Once within a channel, noise receives the same treatment as does the wanted signal. We must clearly distinguish between audio noise and electrical, the latter is not necessarily audible although it often can be made so. Even spots on a television screen are "noise". It is therefore important to keep in mind that the main factors affecting communication over a channel are the bandwidth and the signal-to-noise ratio. The problem is of course that noise in a digital channel may result in some of the symbols received at the distant end being in error.

5.4.1 Probability

Assume that we are at the receiving end of a channel and waiting for binary signals to arrive. At any point in time it is not known whether the next signal will be a binary 0 or a 1, for if it were known there would be no need to transmit the information. The *chances* of it being either are assessed on a *probability* scale extending from 0 to 1 (nothing to do with the binary 0 and 1). There is a fifty-fifty chance of a binary 0 arriving so we assign to this probability a value of 0.5 and the same for a binary 1. This can be expressed as $P_0 = 0.5$ (the probability of a 0 arriving is 0.5) and $P_1 = 0.5$. $P_0 + P_1 = 0.5 + 0.5 = 1$.

Now 1 in probability terms is certainty so we are sure that either a binary 0 or a 1 will arrive but only 50% sure that it will be a 0 or that it will be a 1. If there are four choices, say of a 0, 1, 2 or 3 arriving (expressed by say, 4 different signal levels instead of 2) then the probability for any particular one is 1 in 4, i.e. 0.25. With a pack of 52 playing cards, the probability of any particular card being drawn from a properly shuffled pack is:

$$1 \text{ in } 52 \text{ or } 1/52 = 0.0192$$

so we write:

$$P_{(10 \text{ of diamonds})} = 0.0192,$$

equally

$$P_{(6 \text{ of spades})} = 0.0192$$

and so on.

Thus confronted with 2 choices, there is a probability of 0.5 that we could guess correctly what comes next or 0.5 that we would be wrong.

For 4 choices the probability of a correct guess is 0.25 but for an incorrect guess, 0.75.

For 52 choices the figures are 0.0192 and 0.981, and evidently the probability of being wrong increases with the number of choices. Reasonably therefore, the more choices there are (lower P), the more information is given when the correct answer is transmitted.

5.4.2 Information Content

Take a single signal which can be either a 0 or a 1. From the above, $P_0 = 0.5$, $P_1 = 0.5$ and since the probability for all signals is the same, we can write $P = 0.5$. The information content (I) of a signal is defined in the theory as:

$$I = \log_2 P^{-1} .$$

In this case

$$I = \log_2 1/0.5 = \log_2 2 = 1 ,$$

and this is called a *bit* (of information), the connection with the bit of binary digital data is evident. The formula shows that the information content is inversely proportional to the probability as would be expected from the foregoing Section. What this means in simple language is that one bit of information is needed to distinguish between a 0 and a 1, or in general, between two *equiprobable* events.

Digital data is the simplest form, pulse or no pulse. How do we rate a more complicated signal such as for speech, music, data or television? Here we are faced with continuously varying signals and the information transmitted must simply state the level of the signal at any instant. The first decision required therefore is the number of *sampling* levels needed. This obviously must be greater than the two required in the binary case and yet must not be so large as to transmit unnecessary information – it costs money.

As an example, for speech a simplified approach might suggest that the recognition of 10 different levels of signal power at any instant provides sufficient information. With 10 levels the probability of any particular one occurring at any given time is 0.1, hence:

$$\text{Information content, } I = \log_2 P^{-1} = \log_2 10$$

which we will find is equal to 3.32 and note that compared with $P = 0.5$, $I = 1$, this lower probability gives more information.

5.4.3 Information Flow

How frequently must the samples mentioned above be taken? The theory gives a guide which is that at least one sample is required for each half-cycle of the signal waveform. To conform with this the *sampling rate* must therefore be at least twice the highest signal frequency. Thus for commercial speech with a maximum frequency of 3400 Hz, the minimum sampling frequency is 6800 Hz giving an *information rate* of 3.32 bits (see above) at 6800 times per second, i.e. 22,576 bits per second. (Sampling at 8 kHz is more likely to be used in practice as shown in Sect.5.1.)

Now we must be very clear that what we have just done is, as already mentioned, simplified. It merely leads us to ideas based on the approach by C. E. Shannon (an American mathematician) in order to get information rates for various transmitted signals into perspective. Certainly what is lacking is that there is no allowance for the fact that so many events are not equiprobable, for example, certain letters in a language are much more likely to follow others (in English for example, u is likely to follow q) and again some are excluded (a z is most unlikely to follow a q), thus P is not equal to 1/26 for all letters of the alphabet. Again with a television picture, successive pictures may not change appreciably, the aeroplane in a cloudless sky is a classic example.

5.4.4 Channel Capacity

As mentioned in Section 5.4, noise in a channel can result in errors and the degree to which this happens depends on the signal-to-noise ratio. Accordingly error detecting and correcting codes may be employed but they have their disadvantages, especially in the reduction of transmission rate. The simple error reduction system of parity checking is outlined in Section 5.1.4. This system fails when there are two errors in a block and it is evident that irrespective of the number of symbol repeats sent, some likelihood of error must remain.

The possibility of error is clearly reduced as the number of symbol repeats is increased but concurrently with this the information rate is falling. Thus it would appear that although for maximum security against error several signal repetitions are required, this unfortunately reduces the information rate considerably. However Shannon came to our rescue in the mid 1960's with his now well-known formula (see also Sect.1.2). This shows that this noisy channel problem can be greatly alleviated by ensuring that the information transmission rate does not exceed the rate for any particular channel known as the "channel capacity".

Channels invariably carry noise and the general formula developed by Shannon which enables us to focus on the main features affecting the transmission of information over a channel is:

$$C = B \log_2 (1 + s/n) \text{ bits per second}$$

where C is the channel capacity, B is the channel bandwidth and s/n is the channel signal-to-noise ratio.

Evidently it is not so much the noise level which matters but the degree by which the signal exceeds it. $\log_2 (1 + s/n)$ is given in Appendix 1 for a range of values of s/n so that the noise tolerable in a channel can be calculated for a given rate of transmission. For example, for a commercial speech channel our estimate above of C is 22,576 b/s. Therefore for a channel bandwidth of 3400 Hz:

$$22,576 = 3400 \log_2 (1 + s/n)$$

hence

$$\log_2 (1 + s/n) = 6.64$$

and from Appendix 1, the signal-to-noise ratio is approximately 100 which suggests that the mean value of the signal power should be at least 100 times greater than the mean level of the noise power. These are difficult quantities to measure considering the varying natures of the signals but it can be done.

It is also possible to see how signal-to-noise ratio and bandwidth can be interchanged. Suppose a ratio of s/n no better than

10 is available. From Appendix 1:

$$\log_2 (1 + s/n) = 3.46$$

$$\therefore \quad 22{,}576 = B \times 3.46$$

$$\text{hence } B = 6525$$

i.e. the bandwidth must be increased from 3400 to about 6500 Hz to provide a sufficiently higher quality speech signal to make up for the deterioration due to the increased noise.

A warning here – there cannot ever be a 100% guarantee of complete freedom from error but we can get near it by ensuring adequate bandwidth as above. Also when a high level of security against error is essential, an adequate error correction system must be added.

Here therefore we observe mathematics getting to grips with the multitude of inconsistencies which seem to surround the subject of information flow. Information theory will seldom produce exact answers but we already see its usefulness in providing reminders of the conditions necessary for optimum results. However do not forget that we are only on the fringe of the full theory which in fact requires more high level mathematics than can be mustered here.

5.5 Optical Transmission

We have come a long way since the early days of the transmission of information by light when the Aldis lamp reigned supreme. Morse signals are transmitted by rotating a mirror at the focus of which a light is located. The system has a transmission speed of a few words per minute, a maximum range of a few kilometres but heavily dependent on the vagaries of the weather and useless in fog. Nevertheless optical transmission through the atmosphere is still used for specialized purposes, e.g. military and naval.

Nowadays things are so different, transmission rates are well into the gigabit/sec range (i.e. many thousands of millions of bits in only one second) – and no problems with the weather! Already several optical cables span the North Atlantic and on land optical fibre is now being introduced at an incredible pace.

It is a fact that the invention and subsequent development of optical fibre systems is one of the greatest engineering achievements of this century.

In essence therefore, what we are considering is a transmission system in which the carrier is a ray of light travelling along a threadlike filament of glass (or sometimes plastic for the shorter distances). The transmitter is a device capable of emitting pulses of light which then travel along the fibre to act on a receiver at the distant end. The output of the receiver is in the form of electrical pulses which are a copy of those applied to the transmitter. Most optical fibre systems employ digital time division multiplexing. Although the overall lengths of the systems are digital, there will be the requirement of conversion to and from analogue at the two ends of the circuit if human beings are directly involved.

Concurrently with the development of the fibre itself has been the requirement for the light transmitters and receivers to be able to cope with modern speeds of transmission. There is no point in having a transmission channel capable of working in gigabits per second if, for example the light transmitter is unable to "flash" clearly at this rate.

It is hardly possible to appreciate the digital technology involved in fibre optic transmission systems without first understanding those features of light on which the systems are based. Light is so intangible that it may seem almost capricious. however it is not, the rules are obeyed to the letter.

5.5.1 Light

The light we see is a range of electromagnetic waves such as are used in all radio communication. Until recently it had not been thought of as a bulk carrier of information, we were too busy with long, medium and short waves up to say, 10 MHz, then moving further up the frequency scale to about 1 GHz for mobile services, radar and television. Soon came microwave telephony systems, reaching what is known as the "extremely high frequency" band at some 100 GHz. At this there was a pause until it was discovered that light could also be used as a carrier.

Many eminent scientists have puzzled over the theory of light starting perhaps with Sir Isaac Newton who set the ball rolling in 1666. The idea that light is a form of wave motion then came from the Dutch physicist Christiaan Huygens in 1678. The wave theory was developed further and found to explain much in the field of optics. Nevertheless it still had shortcomings and further research enabled scientists to recognize that light is an electromagnetic phenomenon, not necessarily requiring a medium for its transmission. Then in 1900 the German physicist, Max Planck suggested that the energy in a light wave is not necessarily carried smoothly but only in minute "packets", called *photons* (see also Appendix 6).

This has left us at present with two apparently contradictory features concerning light. These may be generalized as:

(1) when passing through space or a medium (such as glass), it behaves as a wave,

(2) when emitted or absorbed, light behaves like a stream of particles (photons).

In explaining the actions of light we therefore have to choose which feature is better suited, i.e. between the bewildering duality of waves and particles. Furthermore we talk in terms of *rays* of light and draw them as straight lines on paper – it is the only way we have of indicating the flow of a most complex form of energy. Clearly we still have a long way to go for a complete understanding of one of the most essential features of life.

The frequency range, or what we generally call the "visible spectrum" is from about 3.95×10^{14} Hz (red) to 7.9×10^{14} Hz (violet) as shown in greater detail in Figure 5.10. These are truly numbers which we may discuss but are really unable to appreciate fully.

One thing we are sure of however is the speed of light in a vacuum (and generally in air too). It is 2.9979×10^{8} metres per second, denoted by the lower case c and usually rounded to 3×10^{8} m/s. Of interest is the fact that Albert Einstein has shown that this speed is constant everywhere and it remains so however fast a source or an observer may be moving. In more practical terms, when a bullet leaves the gun of a moving aircraft, it does so with the combined velocities of the aircraft and its own. Not so with light however, light from an aircraft travels at c, the

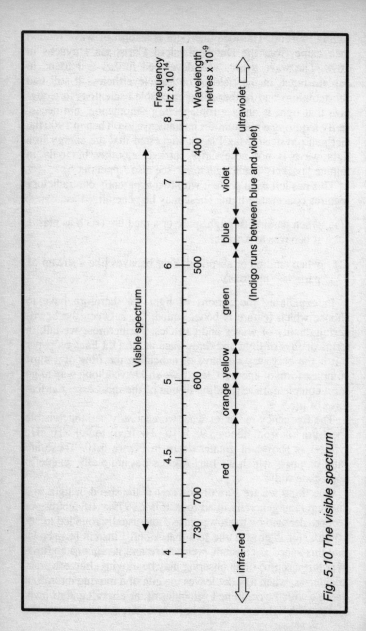

Fig. 5.10 The visible spectrum

speed of the aircraft has no effect whatsoever.

We may also ponder over the fact that light when, for example leaving an electric lamp, does so at full speed, it does not accelerate from zero as things on earth do. We recall however that whatever its form (wave or particle), it is projected from an electron which itself is already moving at an incredibly high speed. Certainly a lot of mathematics is required to sort this one out!

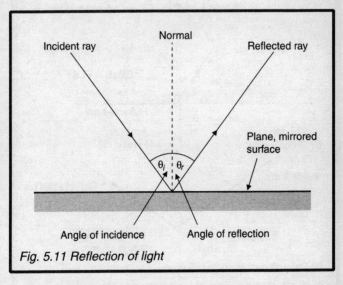

Fig. 5.11 Reflection of light

Some properties of light which are important to us in getting to grips with optical transmission are illustrated in Figures 5.11 and 5.12:

(1) *reflection* – certain materials reflect light very efficiently, up to about 98%, others such as lampblack reflect less than 1%. This quality of a surface in its ability to reflect light is known as its *reflectance* which is defined as the ratio of the reflected *flux* to the incident flux. Here we can simply consider flux as the rate of flow of light energy. We have to admit that reflection is very difficult to explain mathematically but it can be done.

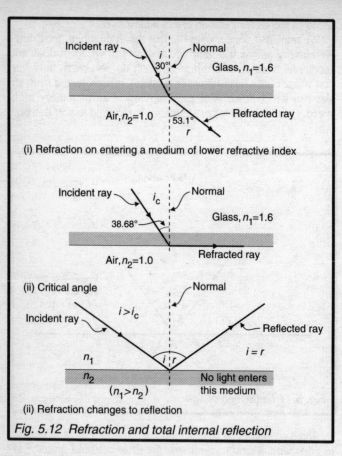

(i) Refraction on entering a medium of lower refractive index

(ii) Critical angle

(ii) Refraction changes to reflection

Fig. 5.12 Refraction and total internal reflection

In considering the paths of light rays, angles are usually expressed at a point relative to the *normal* rather than to the surface which the ray strikes for this may not always be flat. The normal is simply a straight line drawn at right angles from the point of interest as shown in the Figure. The laws of reflection are:

(i)   the incident and reflected rays, together with the normal lie in the same plane;

(ii) the angle of reflection is equal to the angle of incidence.

116

(2) *refraction* – in Figure 5.11 the ray is travelling in one medium only and therefore its velocity does not change. A feature which is of major importance in optical transmission is that the velocity of light (and also of any other electromagnetic wave) falls on entering a more dense medium. The *index of refraction* (or *refractive index*) is the ratio between the speed of light in a vacuum and its speed in a particular medium. It is given the symbol n. The greater the value of n therefore, the greater is the deflection of a light ray on entering or leaving the medium. Labelling the angles to the normal of the incident and refracted rays i and r respectively, Figure 5.12(i) demonstrates how an incident ray travelling in glass which has a refractive index of 1.6 (n_1) is refracted away from the normal when it moves from the surface of the glass into the open air (n_2).

From the work of the Dutch astronomer Willebrord Snell we find that:

$$\sin i \, / \sin r \, = \, n_2 \, / \, n_1$$

In (i) of the figure an incident ray of light is shown arriving at the surface of the glass at an angle, i of 30°, the angle, r at which the refracted ray leaves the surface into the open air, is therefore calculated as follows:

$$\sin r \, = \, n_1 \, / \, n_2 \sin i \, = \, 0.31$$

$$\therefore \, r \, = \, 53.1° \text{ as shown.}$$

Note here that the refracted ray is bent *away* from the normal because the light is moving into a medium of *lower* refractive index.

As the angle of incidence is increased so the refracted ray which has a greater angle, approaches and finally reaches the surface of the glass as shown in (ii) of the figure. The angle of incidence is then known as the critical angle (i_c). By substituting for $r = 90°$ at which angle $\sin r = 1$, in this particular case we find that $i_c = 38.68°$ as shown.

Now suppose that the angle of the incident ray is increased to a value above i_c, it is clear that a ray cannot appear in the air refracted, it is in fact reflected back at the surface as shown in Figure 5.12(iii) and it then follows the normal rules for reflection. The surface of the glass behaves as a perfect mirror to rays arriving at angles greater than i_c. The principle is known as *total internal reflection.*

This is the principle used in optical devices in which reflection of light is required and the losses due to the normal silvering of mirrors is to be avoided, for example in prism binoculars and microscopes. From this we begin to understand how light can travel along a glass fibre without getting lost on the way. The requirement is simply that the incident ray always strikes the surface of the fibre at an angle greater than the critical angle, it is then reflected back into the fibre and not allowed to escape into the surrounding air.

5.5.2 The Fibre Waveguide

Normally in radio communication we eject an electromagnetic wave from an antenna into the atmosphere so that it is either broadcast or alternatively transmitted in a particular direction. When it is essential that a very high frequency wave is delivered to a particular destination with no radiation on the journey, then two main techniques are available. These are the *coaxial cable* with its centre conductor or for even higher frequencies, the *waveguide* which has no centre conductor. Fibre optic systems work entirely on the waveguide principle and we will see that total internal reflection reigns supreme.

Figure 5.13(i) shows a length of a glass fibre and how it can transmit a light ray through total internal reflections, the ray can be considered as bouncing from wall to wall. Note that glass surrounded by air satisfies the condition that n_1 must be greater than n_2 [see Fig.5.12(iii)]. This looks straightforward as a transmission system but it suffers from several disadvantages, perhaps the most important is that two or more such fibres cannot run together. Considering two fibres only in contact with each other, the condition that n_1 must be greater than n_2 does not hold for at the points of contact, $n_1 = n_2$ and light can then travel between the two fibres. There is also the problem that the fibre has to be supported and therefore surrounding it by air all the way cannot be guaranteed. These difficulties are overcome by using a composite fibre consisting of a core of pure glass encased within a *cladding* (i.e. covering) of lower refractive index as shown in Figure 5.13(ii). The dimensions shown are typical of one type of fibre only, there are many others. The fibre is then self-contained as far as the transmission of light is

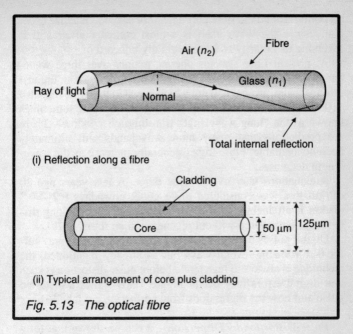

Air (n_2)

Fibre

Ray of light

Normal

Glass (n_1)

Total internal reflection

(i) Reflection along a fibre

Cladding

Core

50 μm | 125μm

(ii) Typical arrangement of core plus cladding

Fig. 5.13   The optical fibre

concerned. Even with its cladding a fibre is truly threadlike for dimensions such as 125 μm (one-eighth of one millimetre) are common. A single fibre of 125 μm diameter might be enclosed in a plastic sheath of outer diameter some 2.5 mm. Comparison of the dimensions of some fibres with those of human hair is often suggested.

There are two main techniques of cladding, resulting in *step-index* and *graded-index* fibres. The step-index is the type we have already discussed, i.e. a core with an abrupt change to cladding on its outside surface as shown in Figure 5.13(ii). The alternative, i.e. the graded-index fibre, is constructed of a material which has a refractive index varying with distance from the fibre axis. Effectively the light rays are being continually bent towards the axis rather than sharply redirected as for the step-index type.

Just one more reminder here – the fibre is of circular cross-section, hence in reality the ray which we depict as a straight line is actually an electromagnetic wave being reflected from all points around the fibre perimeter, not easy to visualize especially since the wave itself is a most complex affair and is reversing its polarity at a rate normally unheard of.

At present fibre systems operate mainly over three wavebands, 400 – 700 nm which as Figure 5.10 shows, is in the visible spectrum, around 850 nm which is just in the infra-red, also 1100 – 1600 nm, well down in the infra-red and sometimes known as the "long wavelength transmission window". There are predictions that many more wavebands will ultimately become available. Fibre losses generally increase as the wavelength decreases.

Attenuations vary over a wide range. A few years ago 20 dB/km loss was considered to be good, nowadays 0.2 – 0.3 dB/km is attainable, such a low attenuation enables long distances to be covered without regeneration en route.

Digital pulses transmitted over a fibre-optic system may suffer distortion in several ways but as already mentioned, the technique is always to regenerate before pulse distortion is such that digital errors may occur. Figure 1.3(i) shows a distorted pulse and how the digressions from perfection are labelled.

Pulse Distortion by Dispersion – it can be shown that for a material which has a refractive index n, the velocity v of a wave through it is $v = c/n$. Now for the glasses used in optical fibres the refractive index is not constant but varies with the transmission wavelength. Accordingly the wave velocity varies similarly with transmission wavelength. This must lead to pulse distortion, said to be due to *material* (the glass) *dispersion*.

Suppose a pulse is applied to such a fibre. Because the transmission must spread over a range of wavelengths (however small), we may consider this as a sum of minor pulses each of a different wavelength, travelling together. Now these minor pulses must travel at different velocities, hence arriving at the distant end of the circuit at slightly different times. Added together therefore the result is a pulse which is spread out, i.e. it has experienced *spreading* because it has propagated through a glass fibre which is a dispersive material. Clearly light sources which operate over a narrow band of wavelengths give rise to less distortion. We will see that a laser diode is superior to a light-emitting diode in this respect.

Information Rate – now we begin to see how for the highest speed systems, dispersion can affect the information rate because of pulse spreading. Suppose that a light source generates waves having wavelengths extending between λ_1 and λ_2. If the delay between the two happens to be equal to half the modulation period (T), then as Figure 5.14 shows, the two waves cancel. This is the extreme case but clearly wavelengths between λ_1 and λ_2 will experience smaller delays and therefore will only partially cancel. This results in a signal variation at the distant end and shows that there is a limit to the range of modulating wavelengths which can be applied to a fibre system.

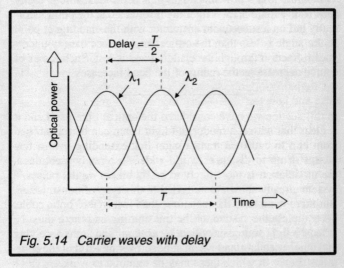

Fig. 5.14   Carrier waves with delay

Scattering – is the process by which light rays are deflected from their true paths by density fluctuations in the core. In the manufacturing process glass molecules are locked into position as the material cools so creating variations in molecular density, hence variations in refractive index. At such variations a light ray experiences *scattering*, the scattered rays proceed along unwanted paths and are therefore lost.

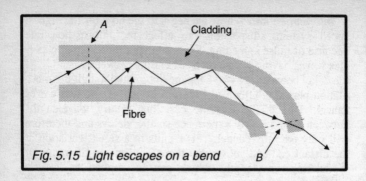

Fig. 5.15 Light escapes on a bend

Bending loss – how this arises in a step-index fibre is easily seen from Figure 5.15. A light ray is reflected at the point *A* correctly but on a subsequent encounter with the cladding at point *B*, the angle is less than the critical angle hence the ray undergoes refraction through the cladding and is lost. Such losses of course decrease as the radius of the bend increases.

In this section we have considered the optical fibre itself and it is clear that with it a modulated light beam can be transmitted from end to end of a transmission link extending over a few metres or up to distances world-wide. As already mentioned, the modulation is most likely to be by binary digital pulses, a system already shown to be suited to this type of transmission. But there is more to the technique than just a fibre-optic cable. To complete the system, at the transmitting end there must be at least a light source or *optical transmitter* and at the receiving end a light detector and we must be forever mindful of the enormous speeds at which these may be required to work.

5.5.3 *Light Sources*
An optical transmitter is therefore a device which accepts a modulated input current and transforms this into a light beam similarly modulated. Such a device must therefore be coupled to the end of the fibre so that there is the maximum transference of light and here we are considering light fibres of diameters in the micrometre range. Light sources generally in use are light-emitting diodes (LED's) and laser diodes.

Light-emitting Diodes – the speed at which they can work, their small size and low power requirements make LED's very useful as optical transmitters. For readers in need of revision on calculations concerning electron energy, please see Appendix 5.

Let us approach this on the simple basis that when a digital 1 arrives at the input, the LED produces a flash of light extending over a narrow band of frequencies but for a digital 0 there is no output.

When power is fed to an LED under forward bias conditions, electrons which arrive in the n-type material are driven into the p-type via the reduced depletion layer. Near the junction and in the valence band, electrons with conduction band energies (see Appendix 5) meet *holes* (we use this term for an atom which is minus an electron and is therefore a mobile positive charge). This is the condition for recombination and when this happens, because each electron has moved down to a lower energy level (Fig.A5.1), it must emit its surplus energy. This it does in the form of a photon, i.e. there is a flash of light (the digital 1). As an example, gallium arsenide (GaAs) is commonly used for the semiconductor, it has a band-gap energy E_g of 1.42 eV (Appendix 7). This is the minimum energy an electron in this material must give up to drop from conduction to valence band.

From Planck's formula, $E_g = hf$ (Appendix 6), we find that λ = 875 nm ($f = 3.43 \times 10^{14}$ Hz) which as Figure 5.10 shows is just in the infra-red region.

Let us sum this up – Figure A5.1 naturally gives the impression that somehow the atoms in the valence and conduction bands lead separate lives. This is because the figure is of an *energy* diagram. In the material all the particles are milling around each other and *collisions* occur with the result that free electrons with conduction band energies recombine with holes so returning atoms to their normal electrically neutral states. However each colliding electron must reduce its higher level of energy in order to recombine with a hole. In certain semiconductor materials this energy (E_g) is emitted as a photon. The radiation intensity is therefore proportional to the diode current.

It is not a simple matter to couple the light output of an LED to a fibre. An extremely accurate joint must be made so that as much light as possible from the LED enters the fibre. A typical

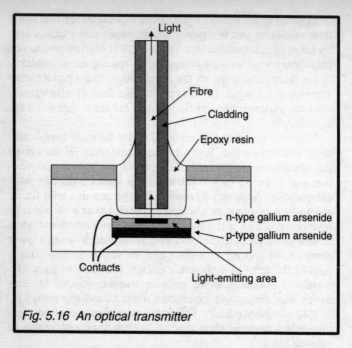

Fig. 5.16 An optical transmitter

method is illustrated by Figure 5.16 and we must remember that the drawing is many times the actual size of the components and the fibre.

Laser Diodes – here we need firstly to appreciate the principles on which the laser is based. LASER is an acronym for *Light Amplification* by the *Stimulated Emission* of *Radiation* and this is just how it works. The main asset of the laser is that it can produce a *coherent* light beam of exceptional intensity through its unique principle of operation. Although Einstein had considered the process theoretically as far back as 1917, the working laser is a comparatively recent development, the first was demonstrated in 1960 by Theodore H. Maiman (an American physicist). This one produced a coherent deep red light beam of such brightness as had never been seen before, it was in fact brighter than the sun. In contrast to coherent light, sunlight covers a broad frequency spectrum (as in Fig.5.10), it is a confusion of many frequencies of electromagnetic radiation, all out of step with each other and therefore incoherent. Maiman's first laser embodied a ruby, not the precious stone but one artificially made. More recent developments, especially for telecommunications purposes, rely on certain semiconductor materials such as gallium arsenide and its derivatives.

Stimulated Emission – the principle on which a laser operates is to raise many more particles into a high-energy state than there are in the *ground* (i.e. unexcited) state. This is known as *population inversion* because it is not the way atoms are normally arranged on an energy basis. The particles are then triggered to fall en masse to the ground state. Photons are therefore emitted as an intense flash of radiation. We next look at this in more detail.

With certain materials there is a *metastable* energy state (stable unless unduly disturbed) as shown in Figure 5.17(i). Atoms can remain with this level of energy for some 10^{-3} seconds before dropping to the ground state and hence emitting a photon (with no metastable state the return is within some 10^{-8} seconds). Note that when there is a metastable state the changeover in energy from excited to ground level takes 10^5 times as long.

Normally an atom can be fully excited on receipt of energy which raises it from E_g to E_f, this is on absorption of a photon of the right frequency. The atom then reverts to the ground state on *spontaneous emission* of this energy. This is a continuous process but with more particles at E_g than E_f. However in the laser, the technique of population inversion results in there being more excited atoms than ground state ones so clearly some means of excitation must be involved. Because the lifetime (the interval between freedom and recombination) of particles at the upper level is long compared with that at ground level, the process results in light amplification (the LA of laser).

Taking the ruby as an example, a tiny percentage of chromium ions is added to introduce the metastable condition. Population inversion is achieved by *optical pumping* from an external light source containing photons of the required frequency for raising atoms to the energy level E_f. Figure 5.17(ii) shows the basic parts of a ruby laser. It is pumped optically by

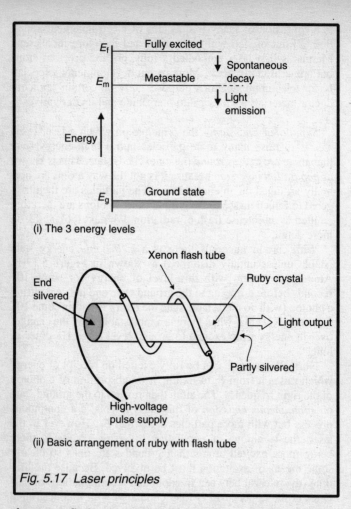

Fig. 5.17 Laser principles

the xenon flash tube. The frequency of xenon light is 5.44×10^{14} Hz producing a photon energy of 2.25 eV (see Fig.5.10 and Appendix 7). This is the energy level of a particle when fully excited. At the metastable level the energy falls to 1.8 eV and this is the energy released as radiation by every chromium ion in the avalanche, resulting in an intense flash of light from the partly silvered end of the rod. A laser operates at a very high frequency but needs positive feedback to keep it going. This is arranged by use of mirrors as shown in the Figure.

There are many other types of laser and in all of them population inversion must be achieved and for this there must be a means of excitation. It is also essential that the basic laser material has a longer particle lifetime at the upper level than at the ground level.

5.5.4 *Light Detectors*

The function of the detector at the distant end of a fibre-optic system is to recreate the electrical input originating at the sending end as faithfully as possible. Clearly therefore the choice of a detector cannot be made without knowledge of the characteristics of the light source at the sending end. As might be expected, the process is the exact opposite of photoemission as is required at the sending end so now we are considering *photoconductivity* instead.

P-I-N Photodiodes – semiconductors rank highly in the practical arrangements, perhaps the one most commonly used is the reverse-biased PIN photodiode. This is a semiconductor diode with an added intrinsic (pure) region sandwiched between p and n. Effectively the width of the depletion layer is increased, accordingly the depletion layer capacitance is reduced, an important consideration at very high frequencies. The reverse bias is naturally less than the breakdown voltage.

On absorbing an incoming photon, an electron within an atom is excited from the valence to the conduction band (see Fig.A5.1), therefore because the electron is now free from the atom, a hole is also generated. Accordingly the photon has generated two charge carriers. We can look at this process on an energy basis. Each incoming photon must be able to provide sufficient energy to raise one electron across the band-gap. Let this energy be labelled E_g, then from Planck:

$$f = E_g / h \quad \text{and since} \quad \lambda = (3 \times 10^8) / f$$

$$\lambda = \frac{(3 \times 10^8) \times (6.626 \times 10^{-34})}{E_g \times (1.602) \times 10^{-19})} \text{ metres} = \frac{1.24}{E_g} \mu m$$

127

where E_g is in electron-volts. From this we can calculate the cut-off wavelength for a semiconductor material provided that the band-gap is known. As an example, for silicon E_g is 1.1 eV, hence the lowest practical wavelength is 1.127 μm (1127 nm, down in the infra-red – see Fig.5.10). In terms of frequency, the highest usable is therefore 2.66×10^{14} Hz.

On the arrival of one or more photons therefore, the material conductivity increases, so also does the diode current. An approximate relationship for a semiconductor diode is given by:

$$I = I_d + I_s$$

where I_d is the dark current and I_s is the light-generated current, showing that the photocurrent is superimposed on the normal dark current which is relatively small.

A typical response characteristic for a silicon PIN photodiode is given in Figure 5.18 from which it is clear that the peak response is at 0.8 μm (800 nm). Germanium has a peak response at a longer wavelength of 1.55 μm and at a longer wavelength still is indium gallium arsenide (InGaAs) at around 1.7 μm.

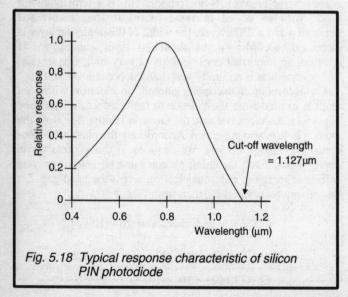

Fig. 5.18 Typical response characteristic of silicon PIN photodiode

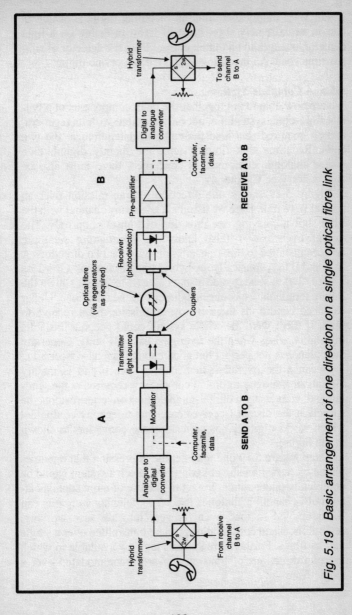

Fig. 5.19 Basic arrangement of one direction on a single optical fibre link

Put very simply therefore, an incoming digital 1 which in fact is an extremely short burst of light, in acting on a light detector, changes to an output current from the detector of similar time span. An incoming digital 0 produces no output.

5.5.5 A Complete System

We are now able to put together the main components of a typical fibre-optic system, i.e. not only the fibre with its regenerators (if required) but also the equipment required at the two ends. Recalling that fibre systems are mainly digital, then where analogue equipment is concerned, there must also be conversion (see Chapter 4).

Figure 5.19 shows one direction of transmission over an optical fibre link. Here we assume a telephony channel with the fibre shown carrying one direction of transmission only. The *hybrid transformers* (also known as *terminating sets*) are devices installed to link transmission-wise the two directions A to B and B to A. Basically the hybrid transformer has a low loss 2-wire (2w) to send (s) and also receive (r) to 2w. As shown the 2-wire terminals are connected directly to the telephone. Under balanced conditions there is no transmission from receive to send, if there were the whole system could become unstable. Instability arises when the *loop* gain exceeds unity. Generally the balance is not perfect but good enough (see also Sect.5.1).

Because the overall system carries speech and is mainly digital, an analogue-to-digital converter is required at the sending end, conversely a digital-to-analogue converter restores the speech at the distant (receive) end. Non-telephony equipment which works digitally has no need of the converters as shown in the Figure.

From Figure 5.19 one may get the impression that one telephone conversation absorbs two fibres. Such a system would be completely uneconomic. In fact by the use of more sophisticated multi-channel techniques (Sect.5.3), telephone circuits can be assembled so that, even for very long distance working, several thousand conversations can be transmitted over a single pair of fibres. Furthermore systems are now available in which the two directions of transmission are accommodated over a single fibre.

Chapter 6

DIGITAL FEATURES OF TELEVISION

Although plans have been announced for satellites to take television completely into the digital era, much still remains analogue. Accordingly because we now realize that digital television is on the way, we, the onlookers, ought here to enquire into what is involved. It is already a fact that much television studio equipment is now digital, so experience has already been gained as to the advantages digital must possess compared with analogue. The television picture has vitality, things change rapidly, the indication being that large band-widths are required for transmission of the signal, hence the possibilities of bandwidth reduction become important.

6.1 The Analogue System

For the benefit of those readers who are not conversant with the electronics of the present television system, a few notes on how it functions may be in order. Let us consider how a television picture is displayed first. The only way in which this is possible is by building up single pictures bit by bit and this must be done so quickly that the viewer is unaware as to what is happening. Accordingly the picture is built up by the efforts of a single tiny spot of light. A very fine stream of electrons is shot from an *electron gun* at the rear of the tube towards the tube face. Here the tiny point of light is produced by the action of the electrons on the phosphors on the inside of the face. Under the control of the *line* and *frame* time bases, the spot moves from one side of the screen to the other at the top, changing its brightness and colour as it goes, all in a mere 64 microseconds. It then quickly flies back to the beginning of the next line below and again moves across the screen. This is repeated until the spot arrives at the bottom of the screen, at this point one still picture has been displayed, all in one twenty-fifth of one second. Within one second therefore 25 pictures have been displayed and as with the cinema, the viewer has the impression of action and movement without realizing that over 10 million *picture elements* have been displayed *each second*.

The incoming television signal is without doubt, quite complicated. Synchronizing pulses are added so that receiving sets and the studio cameras work together. There is also the complication of colour and we have not even mentioned *teletext*!

6.1.1 Colouring the Spot

Fortunately any colour can be made up by mixing together the three *primary* colours, red, green and blue (R, G, B). The camera separates light from the scene into these primaries and directs each to a special pick-up tube. The electrical outputs from the tubes are mixed in such a way that they can be separated later (see below) and the mixture forms the *chrominance* (colour) waveform.

In the receiving cathode-ray tube there are three electron guns, one for each colour. The screen is coated on the inside with microscopic phosphor dots in groups of three. When any dot of a group is hit by an electron beam it glows in its own colour. A special perforated mask ensures that the electrons from each gun strike the appropriate phosphor dot, e.g. those from the electron gun for red are directed only to the phosphor dots which glow red. Each phosphor dot in a group therefore contributes an amount of its colour as determined by the strength of the incoming electron beam. As an example, illuminating the red and green phosphor dots but not the blue in a group produces yellow. Add various small amounts of blue to obtain a range of pastel greens (faintly exciting the green dot on its own gives a pastel green but of the basic shade only).

6.1.2 Putting It All Together

The above may seem complicated but there is more to come. In addition to the colour techniques mentioned above, the system has to transmit the picture luminance (brightness). Although the three colour components contain all the information required for the final picture, they are not transmitted straightforwardly as one might expect, instead they are processed before transmission in order to conserve bandwidth. Firstly a luminance signal Y is generated. This is a mixture of the basic colour components (R, G, B) in certain proportions according to how each contributes visually to the luminance. The red and green components contribute more than the blue (in simple terms they are brighter colours) so a special mixing network is employed to give:

$$Y = 0.3R + 0.6G + 0.1B$$

to result in a colour picture acceptable to most viewers.

There are now four different signals required, R, G, B and Y. However since these are related mathematically, all four need not be transmitted. Having generated Y, two other *colour difference* signals are obtained by taking the red and blue and subtracting them electronically from the Y giving $(R - Y)$ and $(B - Y)$. The remaining component $(G - Y)$ can be derived from these in the receiver. What this all means is that by transmitting the three components, Y, $(R - Y)$ and $(B - Y)$ only, all the luminance and colour information is available in the receiver. With all this to transmit plus the accompanying sound, a television system theoretically requires a bandwidth approaching 8 MHz. This is before broadcasting however and it is a fact into which we will not get involved here that when broadcast using *frequency modulation*, an overall bandwidth of some 27 MHz is required. This is the compromise between the requirements of signal power, noise and bandwidth generally adopted.

6.2 The Digital Approach

When we first consider the bandwidth required to transmit a television picture digitally, the results are certainly not encouraging. The standard adopted internationally for the sampling rate (see Sect.4.2 for a discussion on 'sampling') for the digital formation of a television picture is:

luminance	sampled at 13.5 MHz
$(R - Y)$ colour difference	sampled at 6.75 MHz
$(B - Y)$ colour difference	sampled at 6.75 MHz

this alone (i.e. without sound, etc.) giving a total number of samples per second of 27×10^6.

At 8 bits per sample, which is the number necessary for provision of the full range of 256 levels required to represent a television picture, a bit rate of $(8 \times 27 \times 10^6)$, i.e. 216 M bits/sec, is required. Accordingly a broadcast bandwidth of about half this figure is needed, i.e. some 108 MHz, four times that for the analogue system. As shown above, this seems truly exorbitant compared with that required for analogue television so from these calculations there would appear to be no future for digital television. On the other hand, digital signals can be packed more tightly within a given frequency range because no frequency separation is required to avoid interference between components. In addition noise in the radio path affects digital transmission less, in fact *carrier-to-noise ratios* required for digital transmission are considerably lower than those for analogue, hence lower power transmission can be used.

There is another important facility which is arriving with digital transmission and which results in a much lower bit rate. Clearly a television picture contains much redundant information, for example, a cloudless sky does not change from one picture to the next. Hence, why transmit all this information picture after picture when once could be enough? Accordingly with new digital techniques, the full picture is not transmitted 25 times per second as we now do, but only the *differences* between each picture and the next are transmitted. The bit rate and therefore bandwidth required therefore fall dramatically. Although not so simple to achieve, systems have already been developed which do this so successfully that viewers cannot detect what is going on. The bit rate for such a system may be as low as 30 – 40 M bits/s, an appreciable reduction from the 216 M bits/s calculated above.

Many viewers seem to be quite happy with the analogue television picture at present provided, it seems that comparatively few hanker for the wonders of large-screen high definition television which we are promised. Thus by accepting some picture imperfections, probably not even noticeable by the viewer, bit rates even lower, perhaps down to 6 M bits/s are promised and these provide a picture generally as good as existing analogue systems. At 6 M bits/s, requiring a bandwidth of a mere 3 – 4 MHz, digital television, when it includes all its special techniques, is likely to economize greatly in precious bandwidth.

All this leads to the feasibility of packing more television channels into satellite distribution systems for if we settle for quantity rather than high quality, so many digital channels will be available that the same film can be transmitted on several different channels at once but starting at different times to suit all viewers. All very well but now home viewing equipment is getting really complicated and of course the additional facilities must be paid for.

Digital television therefore has much to offer so we may rest assured that it will surely arrive soon.

TELETEXT is a digital information system already with us. After a picture frame is completed, the spot returns from the bottom of the screen to the top (*flyback*). While this is happening no picture information is being received, accordingly the transmitter seizes the opportunity to send teletext and other data such as weather, news, stockmarket, motoring, programmes. A teletext receiver reconstructs the incoming information and displays it on the screen instead of the normal programme when the user requires. Each teletext page carries up to 200 words.

The teletext data lines are first examined electronically and the digital signals which apply to the page selected by the viewer are extracted and stored in a semiconductor memory. The page is then displayed at the same rate as the normal picture. Certainly a highly complex but successful system.

Chapter 7

DIGITAL NOW AND SOON

While we ourselves remain steadfastly analogue, there is little doubt that much around us is rapidly changing to digital, such are its advantages. Even in the kitchen, washing machines, toasters and microwave ovens are being taken over. Telephones may seem analogue enough but binary digital transmission may soon have its part to play even for the shortest calls.

7.1 Digital Now

Apart from all which goes before in this book, there are many other digitally driven features we might find of interest. The amazing success and future promise of the optical fibre as a transmission or entertainment medium is demonstrated by the fact that even audio and television recording has recently undergone a radical change. The now old-fashioned disc recording and replay has been overtaken by the CD (compact disc). This much smaller device is rapidly invading our homes and as might be expected, it has an enormous information capacity.

7.1.1 The Compact Disc

The disc with its associated equipment is a masterpiece of modern microminiature technology, the disc itself is not miniature but the digital 0's and 1's recorded on it are. In fact there are more than 6×10^9 bits per disc. A single disc can therefore store well over 100,000 pages such as the one we are now reading. The digital information (speech, music, television or computer) is impressed in the disc grooves as a series of pits, each a mere 0.5 µm wide. The disc is read from underneath using a laser beam so that for a digital 1, a pit reflects light onto a photodiode whereas for a digital 0 the absence of a pit results in the reflection of considerably less light. Similar techniques are employed in television film and video recording.

7.1.2 Time

Many of our clocks and watches have already gone digital. Digital clocks which are mains operated rely on control by the

50 Hz mains frequency. This frequency is controlled at the power station so once any clock is set it maintains accurate time. On the other hand a tiny quartz crystal may be used to provide a stable frequency but now this is much higher, e.g. 32.768 kHz. This seemingly high frequency is required because it is preferable to use a higher frequency crystal divided down rather than a very low frequency crystal which is likely to be larger and, in fact, less stable.

A series of flip-flops and binary counters (Sect.3.5.3) is then used to divide the frequency down even to as low as 1 Hz. The rather peculiar figure of 32768 Hz is simply 2^{15} hence dividing the number by 2 fifteen times brings the frequency down to 1 Hz. The 1 Hz pulses are then applied to counters and finally delivered to a digital display.

7.1.3 Telephony and Data

Digital electronic exchanges are now commonplace. They provide clearer and less noisy lines, faster connections and fewer faults. In addition digital transmission is now expanding the capacity of both short and long distance communication systems so encouraging an enormous growth in traffic. Mobile telephones are expanding rapidly and soon digital technology will have taken them all over. These give us a range of features which analogue cannot provide such as greater clarity, freedom from eavesdropping and identification of callers.

Videoconferencing is a term not heard of several years ago yet it is growing in use rapidly. It enables two groups of business people a long distance apart to see and hear each other via television screens – digital is already playing a major part in the facility. Already a world-wide network of computers (Internet) has been set up for interchange of electronic mail, files, pictures and audio.

Digital by power line is now here. Electricity grid power lines cover the country and are quite capable of carrying fibre-optic cables together with the very much larger and highly charged power cables, the voltages and frequencies involved could hardly be more different. It has been established that no interference problems arise. At the top of each pylon exists an earth wire and the fibre cable is wrapped onto it. Operation is at 2.4 Gbit/s, hence the system will be able to provide broadband services of the future. Television and radio programmes are already carried along these lines to local transmitters.

7.1.4 *For the Kiddies*
Computer games are beginning to dominate the toy sector. Children are therefore being introduced to digital at a very early age although it is doubtful whether many of them appreciate the fact.

7.2 Soon
As far as the immediate future is concerned, it is perhaps obvious that many of the digital facilities we already enjoy will be improved and expanded. As an example, there will clearly be considerable growth in information transfer and communications. An increasing number of people will work from home with their facsimile machines and computers. In addition from the home more and more activities such as shopping and personal banking will be arranged by computer, so avoiding the inevitable traffic jams and supermarket queues. As more and more computers invade our homes, foreign languages, usually learnt at school, will be available on computer software. This will provide the spoken language with the written text displayed at the same time on the screen. Even electronic publishing is slowly becoming available now that the compact disc is here. Good quality photographs consume a lot of memory but compact discs have the capacity to handle these in addition to text. Floppy discs on the other hand are hardly sufficient. In the entertainment world high quality digital television will be beamed (even by satellite) to cinemas and other outlets.

The medical profession is already developing "live surgery on screen". With this even keyhole operations can be seen by students without actually being present in the operating theatre. Fibre-optic networks will link hospitals by providing high speed links (say over 30 Mb/s) for high quality pictures so that the smallest detail of the operation can be shown. It all looks wonderful but we must not forget that high speed connections are expensive, even by fibre.

The development of *virtual reality*, unheard of only a few years ago, and involving 3-d will bring us closer to digital even though most of us will be unaware of the fact. It is also said that through virtual reality, computers may help us to perceive things in a richer way in the future. This we await with bated breath and for many, not of an engineering persuasion, with more than a little trepidation.

The experts are in fact already predicting "anywhere at any time to any person".

Digital audio from the broadcasters is also on the way. It will produce CD quality sound without crackle or other interference. Our whole world is slowly becoming digital!

7.2.1 Compression

This, using digital techniques, is already available and clearly it will accelerate the growth of new services. An early compression system was TASI (Time Assignment Speech Interpolation), a telephony system originally developed to increase the traffic which could be carried over undersea cables. In this system a talker seizes a channel only while actually speaking, the circuit is released within a few milliseconds of silent pauses and switched to another talker. The system approximately doubles the number of channels available. It is not a particularly digital system but is mentioned here to indicate how important compression techniques have already become.

For the future, highly complex compression systems are being developed. As mentioned in Section 6.2, television pictures are especially suitable for compression techniques and considering that much television is now transmitted down to us from satellites up above, such techniques are undergoing unprecedented development. Already it has been shown that a single analogue television channel can cater for four compressed digital channels instead with no discernible impairment for most viewers. Perhaps the problem will be that of finding enough material to fill all the channels which will become available.

7.2.2 Replacing the Regenerator

Efforts designed to reduce the requirement for regenerators on long transmission links may result in the use of erbium-doped fibre amplifiers. Erbium is one of the lesser known elements (atomic number 68) and such an amplifier is capable of high gain coupled with low distortion and low noise. Such amplifiers differ fundamentally from the well known regenerator. They work at around 1550 nm (down in the infra-red – see Fig.5.10) and amplify on principles not unlike those of the laser (Sect.5.5.3). Photons of light at 1550 nm are made to interact with erbium ions, causing them to revert to the ground state and in so doing emit another photon at exactly the same wavelength. Now one incident photon has released another and there is amplification. Very briefly explained but we dare not get too involved.

7.2.3 Speech Recognition

So far we have accepted that although a transmission link may be entirely digital, when the human being is involved there is a change to analogue. Attempts are even being made in speech recognition as a means of inputting data to replace the standard QWERTY keyboard. Thus commands and instructions may be spoken directly to the computer without the need of a keyboard. We still have some way to go for hands-free data entry, especially on consideration of the difficulties involved, e.g. the two main forms of spoken English, ours and the American. How different they can be, yet progress is being made, especially in systems which adjust themselves for their particular use.

Appendix 1

CALCULATION OF CHANNEL CAPACITY

The table below lists a range of values of $\log_2 (1 + s/n)$ for values of s/n, the signal-to-noise ratio on a transmission circuit (Sect.1.2).

Table A1 Calculation of Channel Capacity

s/n, db	s/n, ratio	$\log_2 (1 + s/n)$
−0.3	0.5	0.585
0	1.00	1.00
1	1.26	1.18
2	1.58	1.37
3	2.00	1.58
4	2.51	1.81
5	3.16	2.06
6	3.98	2.32
7	5.01	2.59
8	6.31	2.87
9	7.94	3.16
10	10.00	3.46
12	15.85	4.07
14	25.12	4.71
16	39.81	5.35
18	63.10	6.00
20	100.00	6.66
25	316.23	8.31
30	1000.0	9.97
35	3162.3	11.63
40	10,000.0	13.29
50	100,000.0	16.61

As an example, suppose a circuit has a signal-to-noise ratio of 6 dB (i.e. the signal voltage is 3.98 times greater than the noise voltage), then for a 20 kHz bandwidth channel, from the Table:

$$C = 20,000 \times 2.32 \text{ bits per second} = 46,400 \text{ b/s,}$$

i.e. 46.4 kb/s.

Appendix 2

UNIT AND QUANTITY SYMBOLS

Below are given symbols currently in use in the International
Unit System (SI):

A2.1 Basic SI Units

Quantity	Unit	Symbol
Length	metre	m
Mass	kilogram	kg
Time	second	s
Electric current	ampere	A
Temperature	degree Kelvin	K
Luminous intensity	candela	cd

A2.2 Some Derived SI Units

Quantity	Unit	Symbol
Force	newton	N
Energy	joule	J
Power	watt	W
Electric charge	coulomb	C
Electric potential	volt	V
Electric capacitance	farad	F
Resistance	ohm	Ω
Frequency	hertz	Hz

A2.3 Multiple and Submultiple Indicators
These are prefixed to unit symbols (e.g. 15 mA for 15 mil-
liamperes of current).

Multiplication Factor	Prefix	Symbol
10^{12}	tera	T
10^{9}	giga	G
10^{6}	mega	M
10^{3}	kilo	k

Multiplication Factor	Prefix	Symbol
10^{-1}	deci	d
10^{-2}	centi	c
10^{-3}	milli	m
10^{-6}	micro	μ
10^{-9}	nano	n
10^{-12}	pico	p
10^{-15}	femto	f

Appendix 3

TABLE OF POWERS OF 2

n	2^n	n	2^n
0	1	12	4 096
1	2	13	8 192
2	4	14	16 384
3	8	15	32 768
4	16	16	65 536
5	32		
6	64	−1	0.5
7	128	−2	0.25
8	256	−3	0.125
9	512	−4	0.0625
10	1024	−5	0.031 25
11	2048	−6	0.015 625

Appendix 4

SINGLE BYTE BINARY /
DECIMAL CONVERSION

In Chapter 2 is discussed briefly the use of 8-bit (one byte) binary codes. There it is mentioned that there are 256 different combinations of 0's and 1's obtainable from such a code. This Appendix shows them all in a 16 × 16 table (A4.1, page 150) with their decimal equivalents. The latter are in fact not 1–256 but 0–255. Although the table itself is more or less self-explanatory, here are two examples:

Conversion of decimal 219 to binary:
Decimal 219 is found in the third column from the right and fifth line up. The first four bits of the binary equivalent are at the head of the column, i.e. 1101. The second four bits are in the column at the extreme left, fifth from the bottom, i.e. 1011. The full binary number is therefore 11011011.

Conversion of binary 00100001 to decimal:
The first four bits are 0010 therefore the required number is in the third column. The second four bits are 0001 and appear in the second line down of the left-hand column. At third column, second line down is the equivalent decimal number, i.e. 33.

Table A4.1

2nd 4↓ bits \ 1st 4→ bits	0000	0001	0010	0011	0100	0101	0110	0111	1000	1001	1010	1011	1100	1101	1110	1111
0000	0	16	32	48	64	80	96	112	128	144	160	176	192	208	224	240
0001	1	17	33	49	65	81	97	113	129	145	161	177	193	209	225	241
0010	2	18	34	50	66	82	98	114	130	146	162	178	194	210	226	242
0011	3	19	35	51	67	83	99	115	131	147	163	179	195	211	227	243
0100	4	20	36	52	68	84	100	116	132	148	164	180	196	212	228	244
0101	5	21	37	53	69	85	101	117	133	149	165	181	197	213	229	245
0110	6	22	38	54	70	86	102	118	134	150	166	182	198	214	230	246
0111	7	23	39	55	71	87	103	119	135	151	167	183	199	215	231	247
1000	8	24	40	56	72	88	104	120	136	152	168	184	200	216	232	248
1001	9	25	41	57	73	89	105	121	137	153	169	185	201	217	233	249
1010	10	26	42	58	74	90	106	122	138	154	170	186	202	218	234	250
1011	11	27	43	59	75	91	107	123	139	155	171	187	203	219	235	251
1100	12	28	44	60	76	92	108	124	140	156	172	188	204	220	236	252
1101	13	29	45	61	77	93	109	125	141	157	173	189	205	221	237	253
1110	14	30	46	62	78	94	110	126	142	158	174	190	206	222	238	254
1111	15	31	47	63	79	95	111	127	143	159	175	191	207	223	239	255

Appendix 5

ELECTRONS AND THEIR ENERGIES

This Appendix contains a brief discussion on the theory of energy levels within semiconductors. Every electron must possess energy just as does a golf ball flying through the air, its store of energy being exhausted when it becomes still on the ground or perhaps has been expended by breaking a window. We classify the energies of the electron as *potential energy* by virtue of its orbital position (i.e. how far away it is from the atom nucleus) and *kinetic energy* because of its motion – as with our golf ball this energy can be used up by doing work.

For any given semiconductor material there are three bands of energy levels as illustrated in Figure A5.1:

(i)   the *valence* band – this contains the energy levels possessed by electrons in the outermost shells of atoms therefore these electrons are not free to take part in conduction;

(ii) the *conduction* band – this contains the energy levels possessed by electrons which have been released from the orbits of parent atoms, the electrons are therefore available as charge carriers (i.e. for conduction);

(iii) the *forbidden* band – this is the band of energy levels which electrons in a given material cannot have. The forbidden band lies between the valence and conduction bands.

Electrons with valence band energy levels can only be excited to the conduction band if sufficient energy is supplied to them so that they can jump (energy-wise) over the forbidden band. When the energy level of an electron moves from valence to conduction, this must be because it has received additional energy from somewhere which in our case is from a photon of light (see Appendix 6).

Conversely, when the energy level of an electron moves from conduction to valence, energy must have been given up, again in the form of a photon.

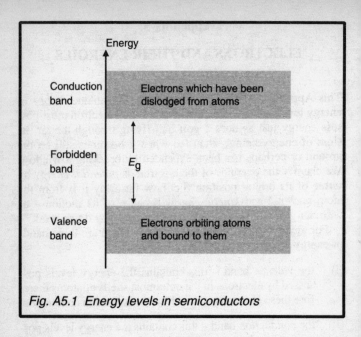

Fig. A5.1 Energy levels in semiconductors

Appendix 6

THE PHOTON

A few notes on the photon may be appropriate. Max Planck (the German physicist) was the first to suggest that light is emitted in tiny bursts or "packets" of energy (note – only energy, there is nothing whatsoever material about light). A little later, Einstein in studying the effect of light on the emission of electrons from the surface of certain metals, considered that somehow a light beam concentrated its energy on the individual electrons. For this to happen the light beam had to be made up of discrete amounts or *photons* of energy. He further suggested that all the energy of a photon could be absorbed by a single electron. Einstein's work agreed with that of Planck in that the energy E of a single photon is given by:

$$E = hf$$

where f is the light frequency and h is Planck's constant, obviously an extremely small number and which is 6.626×10^{-34} J s (joule - seconds).

The photon normally travels at the speed of light but if anything happens to it to change this speed, then it disappears and its energy is given up. As shown above, if a photon collides with an electron, the latter takes up the photon energy and the photon no longer exists.

The following calculation may help our understanding of photons and their energies. The medical profession has examined certain molecules of the human skin and found that an energy of about 3.5 eV (electron-volts – see Appendix 7) is required to break up these molecules and cause sunburn. The lowest light frequency which produces sunburn is therefore:

$$f = E/h = \frac{3.5 \times 1.602 \times 10^{-19} \text{ J}}{6.626 \times 10^{-34} \text{ J s}} = 8.48 \times 10^{14} \text{ Hz}$$

From Figure 5.10 we see that this frequency is just within the ultraviolet range. Lower frequencies have no effect so for an artificial suntan, an ultraviolet lamp is needed.

Appendix 7

THE ELECTRON-VOLT

In this book we are usually considering the energies of extremely small particles such as electrons and photons. The standard unit of energy is the *joule* but this unit is rather large for this purpose. Accordingly for such calculations a more appropriate unit has been developed, known as the *electron-volt* (symbol eV). An electric field is capable of accelerating a "free" electron and one electron-volt is the work done by a field or equally the energy gained by an electron when it is accelerated through a potential difference of one volt. All very complicated but it does result in a more practical unity of energy.

The charge (e) on an electron is equal to 1.602×10^{-19} coulombs and since:

$$\text{work done} = e \times V$$

and V is the field voltage through which the electron has been transported (1 V):

$$1 \text{ eV} = 1.602 \times 10^{-19} \text{ coulomb-volts, i.e. joules.}$$

Never forget that although 'volt' appears in the name of the unit, the electron-volt is a unit of *energy*, not voltage.

Appendix 8

GLOSSARY OF DIGITAL AND ASSOCIATED TERMS

A

ACCESS TIME – the time required in a computer to locate and transfer an item of data from the memory (Sect.3.4).

ADDRESS – a memory location in a computer usually identified by a digital or decimal number.

ADDRESS BUS – a system of wires in a computer emanating from the Central Processing Unit and to which are connected memory and other units. The purpose of the bus is for the CPU to be able to contact any required memory location (see Figs. 3.11 and 3.12).

AMPERE – a measure of the flow of electricity in a circuit. It is the flow of electric charge equal to 1 coulomb per second.

AMPLIFIER – a device which increases the voltage, current or power of a signal.

AMPLITUDE – the strength or magnitude of a waveform, usually measured at the maximum value.

AMPLITUDE MODULATION – modulation of a carrier wave by variation of its amplitude in accordance with the input signal.

ANALOGUE-TO-DIGITAL CONVERTER – a device which changes an analogue signal into the equivalent digital signal (Sect.4.3).

ANALOGUE TRANSMISSION – transmission in which signals vary continuously. An analogue waveform has a physical similarity with the quantity it represents and therefore can usually be expressed by a graph on a base of time.

AND GATE – a digital logic gate which produces an output of logic 1 only when all of its inputs are at logic 1 (Sect.3.1.1).

ARITHMETIC AND LOGIC UNIT (ALU) – the unit in a microprocessor which uses logic gates for arithmetic operations (Sect.3.5.2).

ASTABLE MULTIVIBRATOR – a circuit which produces a continuous rectangular or square waveform. This particular type of multivibrator cannot latch in either state, accordingly it switches regularly between the two states – see also Multivibrator and Section 1.4.1.

AUDIO FREQUENCY – that which can be heard, generally said to be from 20 Hz to 20 kHz.

B

BANDWIDTH – the range between the highest and lowest frequencies in a communication channel or to which a device responds.

BENDING LOSS – in an optical fibre is the loss of light at regions where the fibre is bent (Sect.5.5.2).

BINARY CODE – a statement in binary digits. In computers a binary code is used to represent letters, numbers and instructions.

BINARY NUMBER – of two. A numbering system which has two symbols only, we usually call them 0 and 1.

BINARY POINT – the binary equivalent of the decimal point (Sect.2.1.2).

BIPOLAR TRANSISTOR – a transistor which depends on the interaction between both n-type and p-type semiconductors.

BISTABLE – a multivibrator circuit which has two latching

states. Also known as a *flip-flop*. These are used in many types of computer memory and counter.

BIT – is defined as a 'unit of information'. In digital systems it is a shortened form of "binary digit". It is the smallest digital unit having two states only, generally labelled as 0 or 1.

BIT ERROR RATE – refers to digital transmission systems. It is defined as the number of bits received in error compared with the total number transmitted (Sect.5.1.4).

BOOLEAN ALGEBRA – a special algebra which is used in consideration of logic systems (Sect.3.1).

BPS – bits per second (see *bit*).

BROADBAND NETWORK – a digital transmission network capable of carrying enormous amounts of information and based on fibre-optic cables.

BYTE – a group of 8 bits, sufficient to store 256 different combinations (0 – 255) – Section 2.1.1.

C

CAD – short for Computer-Aided Design – see below.

CAPACITANCE – is the property of two conductors (wires, metal plates, foils, etc.), insulated from each other, whereby they are able to store an electric charge when a potential difference is connected to them.

CARRIER WAVE – a single frequency radio wave which has impressed upon it a band of modulating frequencies. The frequency of the carrier wave is many times that of the maximum frequency of the modulating wave.

CATHODE-RAY TUBE – an evacuated glass vessel in which an electron beam produces a luminous image on a fluorescent screen, especially used in television sets and computers.

CD-ROM – a computer storage device based on the compact disc (ROM = read-only memory).

CENTRAL PROCESSING UNIT (CPU) – a single chip which carries out and controls much of the processing work in a computer (Sect.3.4).

CHANNEL – the path over which information is carried. A channel can be set up on one or more of the following links: an air path, pair of electrical conductors, terrestrial or satellite radio path or optical fibre. A channel is also the conducting path between the source and drain terminals of a field-effect transistor.

CHANNEL CAPACITY – the maximum rate at which information can be transmitted over a channel (Sect.5.4.4).

CHARGE – is defined as a quantity of electrical energy. It is an invisible certain something possessed only by atomic particles. Within the atom protons are said to have a positive charge, electrons negative. The golden rule is "like charges repel, unlike attract".

CHIP – a tiny slice of silicon on which a collection of miniature electrical circuits is etched by photographic and chemical processes. In use it is contained within a plastic case (see also *Integrated Circuit*).

CLADDING – a covering of lower refractive index on an optical fibre (Fig.5.13).

CLOCK – a circuit supplying regular on/off pulses for synchronization of processing circuits in digital systems (Sect.3.5.3).

COAXIAL CABLE – for transmission of high frequency signals. It consists of a flexible copper tube or braiding with a single copper wire running through the centre (Sect.5.5.2).

COMPACT DISC (CD) – the modern replacement for the gramophone record. The disc is much smaller and is read digitally by a laser beam (Sect.7.1.1).

COMPANDING – a system which uses a volume compressor at the sending end of an audio channel combined with a volume expander at the receiving end to reduce the effects of noise.

COMPARATOR – an electronic circuit which compares two input levels and changes its output when either of the input levels exceeds the other (Sect.5.1.2).

COMPLEMENT – refers to binary numbers and is used mainly in subtraction. It is obtained by subtracting the number from zero (Sect.2.3.2).

COMPLEMENTARY METAL-OXIDE SEMICONDUCTOR LOGIC (CMOS) – a metal-oxide semiconductor logic circuit in which one n-channel transistor is paired with a p-channel transistor (Sect.3.3.3).

COMPRESSION – the technique of squeezing more channels into an existing frequency band.

COMPUTER-AIDED DESIGN (CAD) – a computer application especially for engineers, scientists, architects and others for the development of technical drawings.

CONDUCTIVITY – a measure of how well electricity is able to flow through a substance.

COULOMB – the unit of electrical charge. It is defined as the charge transported in one second by a constant current of one ampere.

COUNTER – an electronic circuit, usually comprising flip-flops used for counting binary data at its input terminal (Sect.3.5.3).

CRYSTAL – (short for "piezo-electric crystal") – a tiny piece of (usually) quartz which is capable of controlling the frequency of an oscillator extremely accurately.

CURRENT – the passage through a material of electrons. It is measured in *amperes* and for one ampere in only one second, 6.25×10^{18} electrons pass by.

CYBERNETICS – science of communications and control in living organisms or machines.

CYCLE – is that part of a wave between two successive points having the same value and at which the wave is varying in the same direction.

D

DECADE COUNTER – a binary counter which counts up to 10 before resetting to zero.

DECODING – the recovery of the original signal from a coded form of it (Sect.5.1.2).

DEMODULATION – the process by which a signal (the base-band) is regained from a modulated carrier wave.

DENARY – of ten. The numerical system in use in daily life, more commonly known as *decimal*.

DEPLETION LAYER – a region in a semiconductor material in which there are very few charge carriers, usually at a p-n junction (Sect.3.3.2).

DESCRAMBLER – an electronic device which restores a scrambled signal to normal.

DIGITAL – originally a method of handling information by measuring the amplitude at any instant of a quantity and coding that amplitude in the binary system. Nowadays however many systems work throughout in binary digital.

DIGITAL-TO-ANALOGUE CONVERTER – an electronic unit which converts a digital signal into the equivalent analogue signal (Sect.4.1).

DIGITAL TRANSMISSION – transmission using signals which at any instant assume one only of a finite number of states. In binary transmission there are only two states.

DIODE-RESISTANCE LOGIC (DRL) – logic switching employing diodes and resistors only (Sect.3.1.1).

DISC – a circular thin sheet of magnetizable material used for storing information in digital form (in the computer world also spelt *disk*).

DISK – see Disc. This is the spelling generally used when computers are involved.

DISKETTE – a smaller size, slightly flexible disk, also known as a *floppy disk* when used in a computer.

DISTORTION – is the (usually) unwanted change in form or character of a signal.

DOPING – is the process of introducing minute amounts of a material (the *dopant*) into a silicon slice to produce a semiconductor.

DRIVE – the equipment which reads from and/or writes data to a disk or magnetic tape in a computer.

E

ECHO SUPPRESSOR – a device connected in a telephony transmission circuit for the suppression of echo signals. On detection of a signal in one direction, attenuation is inserted in the opposite direction within a few milliseconds.

ELECTRODE – a metal connector used for making electrical contact.

ELECTROMAGNETIC SPECTRUM – radiations, all travelling at the speed of light and extending in wavelength from very long radio waves to very short gamma rays. In terms of frequency the range is from about 100 Hz up to 10^{22} Hz.

ELECTROMAGNETIC WAVE – the technical name for a radio wave, so called because it consists of electric and magnetic fields moving in unison.

ELECTROMOTIVE FORCE – is a measure of the ability of a source of electricity to drive a current round a circuit. It is measured in *volts*.

ELECTRON – a stable elementary particle which carries (or *is*) a charge of negative electricity. Electrons exist in all atoms and when freed may act as carriers of electricity (Appendix 5).

ELECTRON GUN – an assembly of electrodes for production of an electron beam, e.g. in a cathode-ray tube (Sect.6.1).

ELECTRON-VOLT – a unit of energy used in place of the joule (which is rather large) – see Appendix 7.

ENCODING – expressing a message in code, e.g. when characters are converted into a form suitable for transmission over a digital link (Sect.5.1.2).

ENCRYPTION – is a secrecy system in which frequencies are jumbled so that the transmission is unintelligible except to the authorized user.

ENERGY – is the ability of matter or radiation to do work.

ENERGY LEVEL – one of the allowed energies possessed by an electron in the space surrounding an atom.

ENTROPY – is a measure of the rate of transfer of information in a message. It is therefore the average of the information conveyed by each of its symbols.

EQUALIZER – a circuit which adjusts the overall response of a system to compensate for a particular type of distortion (usually attenuation or phase) over the required frequency band.

ERROR – when used in digital transmission, an error occurs when a digital 0 is incorrectly received as a digital 1 and vice versa.

ERROR-CORRECTING CODE – a code designed for correction of some or all errors arising during transmission of digital information.

ERROR-DETECTING CODE – a code designed to detect some or all errors arising during transmission of digital information.

EVEN PARITY GENERATOR – an error-checking system which adds a single logical 1 when doing so makes the total number of 1's in the byte even (Sect.5.1.4).

EXCLUSIVE-OR GATE – one of the range of digital logic circuits (Sect.3.1.5).

F

FARAD – is the unit of capacitance (symbol F). It is equal to the charge stored in coulombs in a capacitor when the potential difference across its terminals is 1 V. It is an inconveniently large unit in practice so we usually talk in terms of microfarads (10^{-6}F), nanofarads (10^{-9} F) and picofarads (10^{-12} F).

FEEDBACK – occurs when a fraction of the output voltage or current of a circuit (usually an amplifier) is returned to the input. If the energy fed back augments the input signal, the feedback is classed as positive. If it diminishes the input signal, it is classed as negative.

FIELD – the sphere of influence of an electric, magnetic or gravitational force.

FIELD-EFFECT TRANSISTOR – is one which is based on both n-type and p-type semiconductors but the current path is wholly through one type. It is therefore a unipolar device since it depends either on the flow of electrons in the n-type or on the flow of holes in the p-type.

FILTER – a device which passes a limited range of frequencies. There are low-pass, high-pass and band-pass filters.

FLIP-FLOP – a bistable multivibrator circuit used as a memory cell and in arithmetic circuits in computers and switching systems.

FLOPPY DISK – a thin plastic disk coated with magnetic material for storing computer information (Sect.3.4.4).

FLUX – the total electric or magnetic field passing through a surface. Also the rate of flow of light energy (Sect.5.5.1).

FLYBACK – the rapid movement of the spot on a television screen from the end of one line or frame to the beginning of the next.

FRAME – a set of pulses in which each can be identified by the position of its time slot relative to that of a frame-alignment pulse.

FRAMING PULSE – constant-height pulses used for timing events in a multiplex system (Sect.5.3).

FREQUENCY – the number of cycles per unit time of an electric or electromagnetic signal. The unit is the hertz (Hz) which represents one cycle per second.

FREQUENCY DIVISION MULTIPLEX – an analogue system comprising several individual transmission channels, each channel occupying a different frequency band (Sect.5.1).

G

GAIN – a measure of the increase in signal strength when it passes through a system. It can be expressed as the ratio of the power output of the system relative to the power input or more generally as this ratio in decibels.

GALLIUM ARSENIDE – is a grey, brittle material used in high-speed semiconductor applications. It has high resistivity and high electron mobility.

GAMMA RAYS – electromagnetic radiation of a much shorter wavelength than that of light.

GERMANIUM – is a grey, brittle element (atomic number, 32) with 4 electrons in its outermost shell. It is the material in which transistor action was first observed.

GIGABYTE – storage capacity equal to one thousand million bytes.

GIGAHERTZ (GHz) – a unit of frequency equal to one thousand million hertz (10^9 Hz).

GRADED-INDEX FIBRE – an optical fibre made of a material which has a refractive index varying with distance from the fibre axis (Sect.5.5.2).

GRAVITY – the attractive force between any two bodies having mass. There is no explanation of this force, it has been provided by Nature in order to keep all things together.

H

HARD DISK – a metal disk sealed inside a case within a computer – it is a precision device which is capable of storing considerably more information than does a floppy disk. Access to data is also much quicker.

HARDWARE – is the general term for the hard stuff of which the computer and its associated equipment are made (includes keyboard, printer, add-on units, etc.). See also *software*.

HENRY – the unit of inductance defined as the potential difference arising across the terminals of an inductor when the current through it is changing at a rate of one ampere per second.

HERTZ – the international standard unit of frequency equal to one cycle per second (after Heinrich Hertz, a German physicist).

HEXADECIMAL – the use of 16 as a basis of counting (Sect. 2.1).

HOLE – when an electron is removed from an atom, the latter effectively becomes a positive charge and its "vacancy" for an electron is known as a hole (Sect.5.5.3).

I

IMPEDANCE – in an alternating current circuit this expresses the degree of opposition the circuit presents to the passage of an electric current. It is denoted by the symbol Z, with the unit the ohm (Ω).

INDUCTANCE – is that property of a circuit which makes it generate a voltage when a current changes within the circuit or within a nearby circuit to which it is magnetically coupled.

INDUCTOR – is a component having the property of inductance, i.e. there is a self-induced e.m.f. accompanying any change in current.

INFORMATION – when conveyed by a symbol, the information is equal to the uncertainty removed by its receipt.

INFORMATION TECHNOLOGY (IT) – the circulation and processing of information involving both computers and communication systems.

INFORMATION THEORY – is the quantative study of the transmission of information by signals in communication systems.

INFRA-RED – radiation of wavelengths between the microwave region and the visible red, i.e. approximately between 1 mm and 700 nanometres.

INTEGER – a whole number (Sect.2.1).

INTEGRATED CIRCUIT (IC) – a complex electronic circuit consisting of resistors, transistors, capacitors and other components (but not inductors) formed on a single silicon chip (see *Chip* and Sect.3.6).

INVERTOR – another name for a NOT gate (Sect.3.1.3).

ION – the particle which remains when an atom loses or gains one or more electrons.

IONIZATION – the process which produces a positive or negative charge on an atom originally electrically neutral, by the removal or addition of one or more electrons.

J

JOULE – the SI unit of energy, work and of quantity of heat (symbol, J). It is defined as the work done by a force of one newton when its point of application moves one metre in the direction of the force.

JUNCTION – in electronics it is the region of contact between two dissimilar metals which has electrical properties. In telephone systems it is the channel between a local and a trunk exchange.

K

KELVIN – a degree of temperature equal to a Celsius (Centigrade) degree. The scale starts at absolute zero so 0° Celsius is equivalent to 273° on the Kelvin scale.

KILOBIT – one thousand bits of data.

KILOBYTE – in digital processing used to indicate $2^{10} = 1024$ bytes although strictly in the metric system kilo = 1000.

KILOHERTZ (kHz) – a frequency equal to 1,000 Hz.

KINETIC ENERGY – the energy possessed by a body due to its weight and motion.

L

LARGE-SCALE INTEGRATION (LSI) – the manufacture of integrated circuits having between 100 and 5,000 logic gates on a single chip.

LASER – an electronic device which can produce a very narrow, extremely intense beam of essentially monochromatic light (Sect.5.5.3).

LEAST SIGNIFICANT DIGIT – the digit at the extreme right of a number (Sect.2.1).

LIGHT-EMITTING DIODE (LED) – usually a very small electric lamp having no filament. It is in fact a semiconductor diode which emits light when current passes between the anode and cathode terminals.

LIQUID CRYSTAL DISPLAY (LCD) – a display which operates by modifying the transmission of ambient light. The display usually is of black characters on a semi-reflective background. Current consumption is very small.

LOAD – is a device or circuit connected to the output terminals of a signal source and which absorbs power from it.

LOGIC – the arrangement of elements in a digital system for the performance of a specified task (Chapter 3).

LOGIC DIAGRAM – a diagram illustrating how logic gates and associated circuits are connected together to form a complete working system.

LOGIC GATE – is a circuit which provides a logic function. It produces an output of logic 1 or 0 depending on the various states of the input signals (Chapter 2 and Section 3.3).

LOSS – is a measure of the extent to which the amplitude of a signal is decreased on its passage through a system, usually expressed in decibels.

M

MAGNETIC BUBBLE MEMORY – a special type of memory which stores digital data in a string of magnetic "bubbles" in a very thin film of magnetic material.

MAGNETIC STORAGE – digital memories employing magnetic tapes, disks and bubble memories.

MASER (Microwave Amplification by the Stimulated Emission of Radiation) – is a device mainly used for the amplification of very weak signals, e.g. in radar, astronomy and satellite communication. Masers are often maintained at very low temperatures to reduce the effect of noise.

MASS – the quantity of matter (i.e. that which occupies space) in a body as measured by its acceleration under a given force.

MEDIUM-SCALE INTEGRATION (MSI) – the manufacture of integrated circuits having between 120 and 1000 logic gates on a single chip.

MEGABIT – one million bits of data.

MEGABYTE – a unit of information measurement in a memory system. It is equal to $2^{20} = 1,048,576$ bytes, although strictly in the metric system mega = 1,000,000.

MEGAHERTZ – a frequency of 1,000,000 cycles per second.

MEGOHM – an electrical resistance equal to one million ohms.

MEMORY – an electronic store of information in digital form (Sect.3.4).

METAL-OXIDE-SEMICONDUCTOR LOGIC (MOS) – a unipolar system employing n-channel or p-channel field-effect transistors (Sect.3.3.2).

MICROCOMPUTER – a computer small in size and usually portable with facilities for quick programming.

MICROELECTRONICS – production and use of complex circuits on silicon chips.

MICROFARAD – a unit of electrical capacitance equal to one millionth of one farad.

MICRON – one millionth of one metre. The micron is a unit especially useful in microelectronics.

MICROPROCESSOR – is the basic unit on which a computer is built. It can be programmed to perform a wide range of processing functions.

MICROSECOND – one millionth of one second.

MICROWAVE – an ultra-short wave of wavelength less than about 30 cm (frequency, 1 GHz).

MIXER – an electronic device which accepts two different frequencies at its input and produces a combination of these frequencies at the output.

MODEM – a shortened form of modulator–demodulator. These are networks which enable computers to communicate with each other over telecommunication lines.

MODULATION – the process in which a signal is impressed upon a higher frequency carrier wave.

MONOSTABLE – a multivibrator circuit which has a single state to which the circuit always returns.

MOST SIGNIFICANT BIT (MSB) – the binary digit in a digital word which is at the extreme left (also Most Significant Digit).

MOUSE – a small hand-operated device connected by a flexible cable to a computer. The mouse moves an arrow on the screen to select instructions and move objects.

MULTIPLE ACCESS – a system which provides several users with access to the same channel.

MULTIPLEX – transmission of two or more separate elements over the same channel (Sect.5.3).

MULTIVIBRATOR – a special two-stage transistor circuit with feedback so that the transistors switch on and off rapidly. There are three types: monostable, bistable and astable.

N

NAND GATE – one of the range of digital logic circuits (Sect.3.1.4).

NANOFARAD – a unit of electrical capacitance equal to one thousand millionth (10^{-9}) of one farad.

NANOSECOND – a time interval equal to one thousand millionth (10^{-9}) of one second.

NANOTECHNOLOGY – is the manufacture to dimensions or tolerances from 0.1 to 100 nanometres. It is an essential technique in the development of improved electronic and opto-electronic components.

NEGATIVE FEEDBACK – is a system in which a fraction of the output energy delivered by a circuit (e.g. an amplifier) is returned to the input in opposition to the signal there. It is usually employed to increase stability of an amplifying system.

NEGATIVE LOGIC – refers to logical signals and is the condition in which, of the two levels, the logic 1 is the more negative (Sect.1.4.3).

NEWTON – is the SI unit of force. It is that force which when applied to a mass of one kilogram gives it an acceleration of one metre per second per second.

NOISE – any unwanted electrical or audio signal which accompanies but has no relevance to the transmitted signal (Sect.5.4).

NOISE FACTOR – the relationship between the input and output signal-to-noise power ratios of any system.

NOISE FIGURE – the noise factor expressed in decibels.

NON-SIGNIFICANT ZERO – a digital 0 as a sign bit which precedes the most significant digit (Sect.2.1.2).

NOR GATE – one of the range of digital logic circuits (Sect.3.1.4).

NOT GATE – one of the range of digital logic circuits (Sect.3.1.3).

NUCLEUS – the central part of an atom, comprising protons and neutrons.

O

OCTAL – the use of 8 as a basis of counting (Sect.2.1).

ODD PARITY GENERATOR – an error-checking system which adds a single logic 1 when doing so makes the total number of 1's in the byte odd (Sect.5.1.4).

OHM – the unit of electrical resistance, symbol Ω.

OPERATIONAL AMPLIFIER – a very high gain linear amplifier, generally used with negative feedback which can be controlled by external circuits to do a whole range of jobs (Sect.4.1).

OPTICAL CHARACTER RECOGNITION (OCR) – the process of changing printed text into computer data.

OPTICAL COMMUNICATIONS – the use of thin (usually glass) fibres to transmit pulses of light as a communications system.

OPTICAL FIBRE – a very fine glass or special plastic thread capable of transmitting a ray of light, mainly used in optical communication systems.

OPTOELECTRONICS – a subject dealing with the interaction between electricity and light.

OR GATE – one of the range of digital logic circuits (Sect.3.1.2).

OSCILLATOR – an electronic device for the production of alternating electric currents.

P

PACKAGE – the material used to cover and protect an integrated circuit.

PACKET – a sequence or block of binary digits.

PACKET SWITCHING – transmission of messages by dividing them into 'packets'. Packets from different channels are stored and then forwarded in sequence.

PARITY CHECKING – a system used in digital transmission for the detection of errors (Sections 2.1.1 and 5.1.4).

PERIOD – the time taken for a wave to go through one complete cycle.

PERMITTIVITY – is a measure of the ability of a material to store electrical energy when it is situated in an electric field.

PHASE MODULATION – modulation in which the phase of a carrier waveform is varied in accordance with the input modulating frequency.

PHASE-SHIFT KEYING – shifting the phase of a carrier waveform in accordance with a binary input.

PHOTODIODE – a light-sensitive diode which responds rapidly to changes in light.

PHOTOELECTRON – an electron released from the surface of a metal by the action of light.

PHOTON – is defined as a *quantum* of energy, it is a discrete, infinitesimally small amount. The idea is used to explain electromagnetic phenomena when applied to light (Appendix 6).

PICOFARAD – a capacitance equal to one million millionth of one farad (10^{-12} F).

PICOSECOND – a time equal to one million millionth of one second (10^{-12} s).

PIEZOELECTRIC EFFECT – this occurs in certain crystals (e.g. quartz) which when under pressure or tension become electrically polarized in that charges appear on the surfaces.

POLARIZATION – the way in which the electric field of a radio wave is disposed relative to the direction of propagation.

POPULATION INVERSION – the condition within an atom where there are more particles in a high-energy state than there are in the ground state (Sect.5.5.3).

POSITIVE LOGIC – refers to logical signals and is the condition in which, of the two levels, the logic 1 is the more positive (Sect.1.4.3).

PROBABILITY – the extent to which an event is likely to occur (Sect.5.4.1).

PROGRAM – a series of instructions written in a special computer language on which a computer can act.

PULSE – a short duration of voltage or current.

PULSE AMPLITUDE MODULATION – the amplitude of each pulse is commensurate with the value of the incoming modulating wave at the instant of sampling (Sect.5.2.1).

PULSE-CODE MODULATION – the input signal is firstly sampled then a pulse train is modulated by a coded representation of the sample (Sect.5.1).

PULSE DURATION MODULATION – the width of each pulse is commensurate with the value of the incoming modulating wave at the instant of sampling (Sect.5.2.2).

PULSE POSITION MODULATION – a modulation system in which pulses are shifted from their normal (no modulation) positions according to the magnitude of the incoming signal (Sect.5.2.3).

PULSE TERMINOLOGY – see Section 1.4.

PULSE WIDTH MODULATION – see Pulse Duration Modulation.

Q

QUANTIZATION – is the process of classifying samples of an input frequency into a number of adjacent intervals (Sect.5.1.1).

QUANTIZATION NOISE – noise generated within a pulse-code system due to the fact that the exact level of a waveform at any instant cannot be determined (Sect.5.1.1).

QUANTIZING – the process of representing the instantaneous amplitudes of a waveform by steps (Sect.4.2).

QUANTUM – the smallest amount of radiant energy that can be transmitted, e.g. a photon. It is proportional to the frequency of the radiation hence X-rays have many times the energy of infra-red radiation.

R

RADIX – number or symbol used as the basis of a numbering system (Sect.2.1).

RAM – is an acronym for Random Access Memory (see below).

RAMP – a pulse with a sloping edge (Sect.5.5.2).

RANDOM ACCESS MEMORY (RAM) – an integrated circuit containing memory cells for temporary storage of digital instructions in a computer.

READ-ONLY MEMORY (ROM) – an integrated circuit containing memory cells for permanent storage of operational data in a computer. The memory cannot normally be changed or erased (Sect.3.4).

REFLECTANCE – the ability of a surface to reflect light, defined as the ratio of the reflected flux to the incident flux (Sect.5.5.1).

REFRACTION – the effect of the change in the velocity of light when it enters a different medium (Sect.5.5.1).

REGENERATIVE REPEATER – a device which receives a distorted digital signal at its input and produces new clean pulses at the output (Sect.1.4.2).

REPEATER – an electronic device for automatic re-transmission or amplification of a signal.

RESISTANCE – expresses the degree of opposition a circuit presents to the passage of a current.

RESISTOR-TRANSISTOR LOGIC (RTL) – logic switching employing resistors and transistors only (Sect.3.3).

RESONANCE – is the condition in which an oscillating circuit or vibrating object responds with maximum amplitude to an applied periodic force.

RIPPLE COUNTER – a counter in which the output of each flip-flop initiates a change in the next adjoining one (Sect.3.5.3).

ROM – is an acronym for Read-Only Memory. This is the memory area in a computer reserved for the information and instructions which can be read any number of times but not changed.

ROOT MEAN SQUARE (r.m.s.) VALUE – this is the value of a steady d.c. current which has the same heating effect as the current in question. As an example, the r.m.s. value of the electricity mains voltage is 240 V whereas it has a peak (i.e. maximum) value $\sqrt{2}$ times this, i.e. about 340 volts.

S

SAMPLING – measures the amplitude of an analogue signal at regular intervals for conversion to digital form (Sect.4.2).

SCANNING – the resolution in a prearranged pattern of a television picture into its elements of light and colour.

SCATTERING – the deflection of light rays through density fluctuations in an optical fibre (Sect.5.5.2).

SCRAMBLING – is a method by which frequencies in a transmission are jumbled so as to make the outcome unintelligible except by the intended recipient(s).

SEMICONDUCTOR – a solid material which has a conductivity above that of an insulator but below that of a conductor.

SEQUENTIAL ACCESS – winding of a magnetic tape to the section required (Sect.3.4.4).

SEQUENTIAL LOGIC – a digital memory circuit based on flip-flops used in logic counters and memory systems.

SHIFT REGISTER – a register in which data is fed in serially, moving along one bit at a time as more data is entered (Sect.3.5.1).

S.I. (SYSTÉME INTERNATIONAL d'UNITÉS) – is the internationally agreed system of units for mechanics, heat, illumination and electrotechnics.

SIGNAL – an intelligible sign which conveys information.

SIGNAL-TO-NOISE RATIO – the ratio of the average power of a signal to that of the noise accompanying it.

SIGN BIT – a bit added to a binary number to indicate whether the number is positive or negative (Sect.2.1.2).

SOFTWARE – a general term for the programs and instructions which control the hardware of a computer (see also *hardware*).

SPECTRUM – the range and distribution of the frequency components of a signal.

STEP-INDEX FIBRE – an optical fibre having a core with an abrupt change in refractive index to the cladding (Fig.5.13).

STORAGE – memory within a computer which permanently stores information.

SUPERHIGHWAY – see *Broadband Network*.

T

TELECOMMUNICATIONS – communication from afar. The use of electronic equipment to transmit information via wires, fibre, the atmosphere and space.

TELEMETRY – the transmission, usually by radio, of measurements made at a distance.

TERMINATING SET – a circuit consisting mainly of transformers used to couple a 2-wire transmission line to a 4-wire system (Sect.5.5.5).

THERMAL NOISE – electrical noise which arises in a conductor from the agitation of particles due to heat.

TIME BASE – an electronic circuit for generating a repetitive timing voltage.

TIME CONSTANT – is a measure of the rate of rise or fall in the value of a unidirectional quantity when electrical conditions change. As an example, the time constant of a capacitor is the time taken for the voltage across it to rise from zero to 0.6321 $(1 - 1/e)$ of its final value.

TIME-DIVISION MULTIPLEX – a multiplex system in which the individual signals occupy separate time slots. The full bandwidth of the system is made available at regular intervals to each of the separate input signals (Sect.5.3).

TRANSDUCER – a device which changes one form of energy into another. As an example, a microphone changes acoustical energy into electrical energy.

TRANSFORMER – an electromagnetic device usually employed for changing one voltage into another or for matching two unequal impedances.

TRANSISTOR-TRANSISTOR LOGIC (TTL) – a digital system, based on bipolar transistors which provides logic and counting functions (Sect.3.3.1).

TRUTH TABLE – a table showing how a particular digital logic circuit performs for all possible combinations of input signals.

TUNED CIRCUIT – an electronic circuit which resonates or "tunes" to one particular frequency (or narrow band of frequencies) only.

U

ULTRA-HIGH FREQUENCY (UHF) – radio waves with frequencies in the range 300 MHz to 3 GHz.

ULTRASONIC WAVES – sound waves at frequencies above about 20 kHz which are inaudible to the human ear.

ULTRAVIOLET – radiation having wavelengths above the visible spectrum (say, above 400 nm) up to the X-ray region (2 nm).

UNIPOLAR TRANSISTOR – a transistor depending on either n-type or p-type semiconductor materials, e.g. as in a field-effect device.

V

VIDEO – that which we can see. A term used with regard to television (e.g. video camera, video tape), videoconferencing, and any system transmitting pictures by telephony channels.

VIDEO DISC – a disc on which picture and sound are recorded in digital form.

VIDEO DISPLAY UNIT – the screen and keyboard of a computer.

VIDEO TAPE – a magnetic tape, contained in a video cassette, on which sound and vision are recorded.

VIRTUAL REALITY – simulation by computer of objects in three dimensions.

VOLT – a measure of the difference of electric potential between any two points in a circuit.

W

WATT – the unit of electric power equal to the rate of conversion of energy of 1 joule per second.

WAVEFORM – the shape obtained by plotting the amplitude of an electrical signal against time on a graph.

WAVEGUIDE – a metal tube of rectangular or circular cross-section through which microwaves are transmitted (Sect.5.5.2).

WAVELENGTH – the distance between one point on a wave and the next corresponding point.

WORD – a series of digital bits as a single unit of information, e.g. one byte is an 8-bit word (Sect.2.1.1).

Z

ZENER DIODE – a semiconductor diode with a p-n junction with heavy doping on both sides. The diode is used in the reverse direction. When the Zener breakdown voltage is reached the reverse current increases sharply and the voltage across the device remains practically constant. The diode is therefore used as a voltage regulator.